WHAT'S THE WORLD COMING TO?

What's the World Coming To?

SCIENCE LOOKS AT THE FUTURE

A. M. LOW

FORMERLY HONORARY ASSISTANT PROFESSOR OF
PHYSICS, ROYAL ORDINANCE COLLEGE

With illustrations by
HENRY HEWITT

1951

J. B. LIPPINCOTT COMPANY

PHILADELPHIA AND NEW YORK

Library of Congress catalog card number 51–11194

DEDICATED TO
D. L. BITTON

CONTENTS

INTRODUCTION

FOR every person in the past who has been too optimistic about future scientific developments there have been a million who were far too pessimistic. Only a handful of men actually believed that Orville Wright had flown, even after that first historic day was over. Editors refused to print the news on the ground that it was laughably improbable. Far from creating a sensation, the first flights hardly caused a ripple of interest throughout the world and it was years before millions knew what had happened. Even then it is doubtful if many realised the significance of the event, not for their grandchildren, but for themselves.

Before you pass judgment, therefore, on any forecast, think on those that have been delivered in the past, not by ignorant, uneducated peasants, but by experts who suffered not from lack of knowledge, but from prejudice and lack of imagination. Here are some of the things they said:—

"The demonstration that no possible combination of known substances, known form of machinery and known forms of force can be united in a practicable machine by which we will fly long distances through the air, seems to the writer as complete as it is possible for the demonstration of any physical fact to be. May not our mechanicians . . . be ultimately forced to admit that aerial flight is one of the great class of problems with which man can never cope, and give up all attempts to grapple with it?" *Simon Newcomb, the American scientist, writing at the turn of the century.*

"A man of thirty indeed may see the feat accomplished [flying the Atlantic], but for myself I think the probabilities are rather against than for it." *Frank Hedges Butler, noted aeronaut and friend of Wilbur Wright, writing in 1910. The Atlantic was flown nine years later.*

"I do not think that a flight across the Atlantic will be made in 'our time,' and in our time I include the youngest readers . . . moreover, owing to the lightness of the air as a medium in which the airplane has to operate, I do not think it will ever be used for carrying either goods or a large number of passengers." *The Hon. C. S. Rolls, motoring and flying pioneer.*

"Even if the propeller had the power of propelling the vessel, it would be found altogether useless in practice, because the power being applied at the stern, it would be impossible to make the vessel steer." *Sir William Symonds, Surveyor of the Royal Navy in 1836, shortly after the screw propeller was patented.*

"A man about 46 years of age has been arrested in New York for attempting to extort funds from ignorant and superstitious people, by exhibiting a device which he says will convey the human voice any distance over metallic wires. He calls the instrument a 'telephone' which is ob-

viously intended to imitate the word 'telegraph' and win the confidence of those who know of the success of the latter instrument. Well-informed people know that it is impossible to transmit the voice over wires and that, were it possible to do so, the thing would be of no practical value."
Editorial in Eastern newspaper (U.S.A.), 1865.

"The Board of Admiralty were of the opinion that they [airplanes] would not be of any practical use to the Naval Service." *A letter from the First Lord of the Admiralty to the Wright brothers in 1907.*

"On behalf of the Aero Club I went with a deputation to the War Office offering to lend two machines for the manœuvres and was rebuffed by them saying that they did not see any uses for aircraft in war." *Lord Brabazon of Tara.*

"There is a man here who proposes to light the streets of London with smoke." *Sir Walter Scott, commenting on the proposal to have gas street-lighting.*

"With regard to electric light, much has been said for and against it, but I think I may say without fear of contradiction that when the Paris Exhibition closes electric light will close with it and very little more will be heard of it." *Professor Erasmus Wilson in 1878.*

Is this enough? Or do you wish to be reminded that witches were burned at the stake, on the evidence of children, a few hundred years ago; that the use of anaesthetics only a century ago was bitterly opposed on religious grounds; and that the theory of bacteria was laughed to scorn? "When pigs fly" was not so long ago a way of describing the impossible. Now when passengers who have flown the Atlantic are asked if they had a good trip they sometimes say—"Quite good, but the soup for dinner was cold."

Nothing delights the ordinary man more than to prove a prophet wrong. The way of a prophet is, indeed, likely to be thorny. When he makes his prophecy he can expect to be jeered at; future developments only too often seem fantastic or absurd. If in due course the prophecy proves wrong, the "wise man" can be told, "There, I told you so!" If he proves right, the prophet is by that time generally dead and in any case is often forgotten. This is a penalty which must be borne by any book devoted to all that is bound to happen.

But it is not the first time. About twenty-five years ago *The Future* had a mixed reception and even the most favourable reviews spoke of "fantasy." The less favourably inclined suggested anything from "sensationalism" to drunkenness. What is interesting to-day is not the reviews, but the fact that the great majority of the forecasts then made are now commonplace. Television, radar, rockets, 600 m.p.h. planes, artificial insemination, contact-glasses, operations on the brain for restoring sanity; these are no longer "fantasies," but everyday things understood by Macaulay's proverbial schoolboy, if not always by his father.

This is not a matter of boastfulness. There were sufficient errors of under-estimation as well as over-estimation in an already humiliating world to show that the real difficulty in gauging the future is not one of limiting the imagination to prevent forecasting becoming fantasy, but to conceive of sufficiently far-reaching developments. There are to-day a hundred "babies" of invention which in a century or less will become giants and perhaps revolutionise the way of life of the greater part of mankind. How can we distinguish the promising babies from those that will not survive childhood? How can we see their ultimate growth and the children to which, in turn, they will ultimately give birth?

Look back a hundred years and you will see the problem. There existed then inflammable oils, the means of producing electric sparks, alloyed steels, india-rubber, all the ingredients, in fact, of a modern car. Yet no one seriously conceived the idea of a motor-car, or thought that in a comparatively short time motors would revolutionise our method of transport by land, sea and air or make possible warfare on a scale never known before. They did not realise it even fifty years ago when hundreds of motor-cars were already in existence. When in the nineties that master of prophets H. G. Wells wrote of the future developments of warfare, it was not the motor that he mentioned but the bicycle! The bicycle, he thought, was going to revolutionise warfare by making possible speedy transport. He pictured the war of the nineteen forties being fought by hundreds of thousands of soldiers on bicycles.

How did he fall into this error? Why did he think that this was bound to happen instead of a development that had already begun under his nose? The answer, perhaps, is that he was unduly impressed by the developments of the bicycle which had just taken place so that he was sceptical of the possibilities of the then comparatively feeble and unreliable internal combustion engine. He did not realise that the bicycle was, from the point of view of development, virtually a "dead end" while the internal combustion engine had possibilities to the point where it would prove more important than any locomotive.

A hundred years ago the stationary steam engine was so impressive that people could not visualise a vehicle driven by an internal combustion engine although it could have been built from existing materials without difficulty. Inconvenient and inefficient on roads designed for horse traffic, motor-cars were thought to have no real future and the steam engine driven coaches of early days did little to remove this impression. The idea that road transport would ultimately be revolutionised by an engine operated by a series of "explosions" did not occur, just as to-day the absurdity of the present form of reciprocating motor causes no surprise.

This is but one example of the difficulties presented by

any type of forecast, technical or otherwise. It would indeed be surprising if worse mistakes were not made. But a reading of the "scientific" prophecies of the past suggests that it is much easier to under-estimate than to over-estimate any development. The telegraph was scorned by the Royal Navy on the ground that signalling by flags was perfectly satisfactory. A few decades later that service was saying that wireless telegraphy was of no interest or value. Experts rejected the absurdity of the screw propeller and again it was not until long after their possibilities had been appreciated by others that naval engineers realised the revolution which the torpedo and submarine could work.

Our Navy was not impressed by controlled torpedoes in the 1914 war. Electrically controlled rockets were turned down in 1916, magnetic or acoustic mines were not foreseen, self-sealing petrol tanks were long delayed and the battle of the land tank has become a classic example of prejudice. The very introduction of steam to the Navy was fought to the end. We have in England no official department which asks the public to submit inventions. Only the U.S.A. seems determined *not* to fight future wars in terms of the past.

Dramatic future developments are usually not foreseen because there is a tendency to condemn or greatly under-estimate an invention in its initial and often imperfect stage. Consider two examples. It seems unfair to select H. G. Wells again, because he was so often right and did so much to arouse interest in scientific prophecy, but his mistakes are more interesting for this very reason. In 1900 he suggested there was no future for the submarine in warfare. He spoke of its blind gropings under the sea and thought the most it could achieve was the torpedoing of a battleship hulk at anchor in a harbour, but that its own crew was more likely to be suffocated. Sixteen years later the submarine nearly brought Britain to her knees. Here Wells's error seems to have been due to failure to see that

the submarine would be transformed from a blind, grop-
ing, slow-moving thing into a very destructive weapon by
the use of two inventions that already existed: the peri-
scope and the diesel engine.

Thirty-six years ago not much was thought of the possibilities of television. The most practical systems involved
many contacts, whirring discs or even mechanical syn-
chronisation between transmitter and receiver. It all
seemed wonderful but very clumsy. The perfection of the
cathode ray tube, not a new invention, and its adaptation
to television, changed the whole outlook. The crudity of
early television did not deceive the scientific forecaster.
He knew it was on its way because it was a logical development from the discovery of how to transmit signals by
modulating waves in the aether, combined with certain
other electron discoveries. What he could not say, with
equal certainty, was when it was bound to happen.

This book looks forward for twenty-five, fifty and a
hundred years. As a preliminary exercise it is worth-while
to take the mind back for similar periods, for it emphasizes
how great are the changes that can happen in a comparatively short time. A hundred years ago there were
very few of the thousands of things we take for granted
to-day, from electric lighting and power, to motor transport. The telephone was unknown. The real steam turbine had not been invented. High explosives had yet to
come. None of the weapons of modern warfare was
known; no machine-gun in its many forms, no high velocity
rifles and artillery. Ships were built of wood; another
twenty years were to pass before armour plating was seriously considered. No aeroplane had flown. In fact no
lighter-than-air craft under power had flown. Balloons
were for sport and had no very serious future. There was
no chemical industry based on synthesis. Large scale canning of food or refrigeration was unknown. Anaesthetics
were a novelty, only one, and that rather dangerous, being

in common use. Surgery was a gamble in which most patients died. Antiseptics and asepsis were unknown. Main
water and drainage were still novelties. Light came from
candles and oil lamps.

But it would be easy to continue for several pages with
the things that were unknown. You realise all this; you
say, "What is the point of it?" It is that in looking forward
we must always bear in mind that life in 1950 will soon
seem as primitive and lacking in the simplest amenities as
life in 1850 does to us to-day. A voyage to the moon, at
least superficially, presents fewer difficulties than did an
air voyage between Europe and America in eight hours in
1850. The complete eradication of certain diseases at
present incurable appears no more absurd to us than
X-rays would have been to the people of 1850.

Of course, you may argue, it cannot be "proved" that
scientific material progress will continue at the rate it has
averaged over the last century. No, it cannot be "proved."
It is possible to fall into grave and even absurd errors
simply by producing the curve of progress without considering other factors. But in the light of the last hundred years the weight of probability seems to be either that
scientific, or material, progress will continue at an accelerating rate or that it will end altogether in some great
catastrophe. Failure must be considered as a bare chance,
and we can safely confine ourselves to forecasts upon the
present indication that full progress based on scientific
method will continue.

This glancing back is important in order to balance the
opportunities of the future and it is not necessary to look
into history so remote as 1850. Go back only twenty years,
less than a generation, and consider other things that we
take for granted to-day which were then unknown or
unfamiliar. They include television, radar, fluorescent
lighting, most of the plastics, scores of everyday drugs,
including the sulpha group and penicillin, bonded ply-

woods, many kinds of synthetic boards and synthetic rubber. There was no air passenger service across the Atlantic. Many of the operations performed by surgeons, notably on the heart, were undreamed of. "Streamlining" was just beginning. This is a brief list jotted down. In fact, in only twenty years there have been vast changes. We must not rule out the possibility of similar change in the next twenty years when inventions still in their infancy come to maturity. Indeed we know definitely that they will come, for the same circumstances of development have repeated themselves for many thousand years.

There is one very specialized kind of forecasting based upon statistics. It is possible to forecast how many men, women and children will be living in ten or twenty years and to do it with considerable accuracy. Alarmed at world population growth, or lack of growth in certain countries, there has been much calculation of this kind. We are told that the population of the world will be 4,000 million in so many years or that the population of Britain will fall to twenty million in a hundred years' time. The expert, of course, always prefaces his forecasts with "if the present trends of population continue," but this phrase is apt to be forgotten in discussion. Moreover, while the population for twenty years ahead may be predicted with considerable accuracy, because the vast majority of people concerned are already in existence, to continue the line indefinitely on the assumption that present trends will continue is quite absurd.

Any tendency, represented graphically and continued to infinity or zero, of forecasts that the population of the world will be infinite or that of England zero, must be wrong. Obviously the trend will change at some point. Statistics do not help you to discover when this point is likely to be, although the statistician may discover "cycles," in other words draw conclusions from the past. He has then departed strictly from the irrefutable world of figures and entered that of a different kind of forecasting, so that if he treats his cycles or guesses of the moment in the same respect as his factual figures, he may fall into great error. A forecast of the population of Britain, or that of the world, for ten years hence might not be more than one or two per cent wrong, but a forecast for a hundred years hence, based upon one tendency, might show ten, twenty or an even greater percentage of aberration. Human beings can be represented as ciphers, but they can never be treated in the sense of tons of coal or bags of flour.

The question of recurrence is worth consideration in any future outlook; clearly, if everything developed in this manner our task of seeing into the future would be very easy. Enthusiasts for repetitive change have discovered periods of varying length in everything from the suicide rate to the wholesale price index. The theory of the historical cycle is that there is a rise for a period to a peak and then a fall to a trough; plotted graphically the result is a series of waves, and if it is assumed to continue, it is possible to forecast with accuracy such events as the suicide rate in ten or twenty years, the index for wholesale prices in 1980, or the level of industrial shares on the stock exchange in A.D. 2000.

We need not be too sceptical of this statistical juggling, although sometimes its results could be expressed more simply by saying that most things tend to return to their average. Such figures are well worth study and the evidence for some business cycles is impressive. But there are a number of points that we should note before we say that something is bound to happen because a curve says so. The first is that we must distinguish between established facts, natural phenomena and changes in human behaviour. There is an obvious cycle of the seasons, based on the movements of the earth, and we should be mad not to take it into account, toying with the idea in summer, for instance, that winter might not come.

The most interesting of these particular periodic seasons is that for the maxima and minima of sunspots. This, it is claimed, has been traced for many years and there is evidence that it has far-reaching effects; a maxima of sunspots means more electro-magnetic storms on the earth with obvious interference in radio communications, less "radiation," perhaps more rainfall. Although, therefore, we may expect the recurrence of phenomena with rainfall or sunshine, crop variation would be small compared with that which might be expected from the use of a new fertiliser, a new way of using fertilisers, or a new method of controlling insect pests.

Other regular changes, such as that of the living numbers of fur-bearing animals, or the incidence of epidemics, may or may not really exist. Once we are determined to find a cycle it is so easy to make the figures fit. Even if established, they would be of small importance in long-range forecasting; the five-, ten- or twenty-year dwell of incidence of an infectious disease might be of trifling moment compared with the discovery of a novel drug.

None of the forecasts in this book is based upon mathematically expected changes; and although the study of these "waves" may be considered increasingly important in the future, it is possible that their interpretation will be quite different in principle. It may be found that the "cycle" is no more than the working of a cause and effect. The slump and boom of trade, for example, may not be based on a natural law but, more simply, on the natural tendency to over-produce things in demand and under-produce, as a result, later. In other words the economic frequency may be the battle between the two sides of man, the cautious and enterprising, the optimistic and the pessimistic, the result being like alternating current, with the peaks occurring every few years instead of many times a second.

Long-distance forecasting cannot take account of these

conditions which often occur at different levels; there may
be good and bad periods in trade, but the amount of trade
in the trough of the most recent wave may be greater than
that at the peak of a wave a few periods back. The one
change that might appeal to the long-distance scientific
forecaster is the expectation of "prosperity ratio." It has
been pointed out that about every fifty years a great and
almost sudden expansion of prosperity in the widest sense
has occurred, always associated with some great invention.
A new cycle is due to begin in the middle of this century
and it is interesting to speculate with which particular
invention this exploitation could be associated.

The common guess would, no doubt, be that it will be
based on the most spectacular discovery of the age, atomic
fission, but it is more likely to be connected with the development of the electronic devices which have been
brought to perfection in the last ten years and which now
await mass production and full use. Previous trade ex-
pansions have generally been associated with steam power
applied to factories at the end of the eighteenth century,
the construction of railways, the rapid growth of communications in the middle of the nineteenth century and
the construction of motor transport with the exploitation
of electrical power at the beginning of the present century.

The method of forecast employed in this book is of another kind. It deals with tendencies and the probable
course of events rather than exact dates or descriptions of
future events in detail. How easy it is even for the imaginative prophet to be wrong in dates was shown again when
H. G. Wells, very daring in the face of contemporary scep-
ticism, took a chance in saying that heavier-than-air machines would have flown for the first time by 1940. In fact
the Wright brothers flew only a few years after his pro-
nouncement. At the same time Wells was prophesying
that by the middle of the century the railways would have
disappeared except for a few rusty mineral trains clanking

towards over-grown sidings. Wells was a trained biologist and not a trained engineer, otherwise he might have seen that one or other of these forecasts must have been wrong.

If the internal combustion engine was to develop to the stage where it would drive the railways out of business, it could obviously be adapted as a power plant for heavier-than-air flight; it was the "missing link" which experimenters needed. The forecaster of the future should not be a specialist or he will be in danger of seeing the development only of his own branch of science. But we cannot blame Wells for, as we have seen, Newcomb also explained the impossibility of flight, although within a year or two the Wright brothers were to fly with perfect success.

To examine the future without prejudice we must first admit that nothing is impossible. But we must also see that every development comes logically from that prevailing before. Atomic fission, as it was understood in 1945, was a logical development from the academic discoveries of Lord Rutherford; although in 1930 one could forecast that atomic fission would be achieved, the date of this result could not be stated with any accuracy. Indeed, the indications were that the necessary research would occupy nearly fifty years. But for the needs of war, realisation might have taken fully this period, and the important fact to note is that the work of atomic scientists from 1942 to 1945 was not revolutionary but evolutionary. Anything forecast for the next hundred years is already in existence in some form. This does not mean, for example, that we could send a rocket to the moon next year if we devoted sufficient resources to its construction or that surgeons could operate upon a criminal and turn him into a good citizen if the opportunity arose. It implies, simply, that the basic inventions and knowledge are there and that they point to the realisation of actuality in the future.

The time taken to exploit knowledge is often a matter of apparent caprice. The chance that atomic fission was discovered in 1945, or more correctly, demonstrated on a large scale for the first time, has determined the decision of the industrialised world to expend a great part of its available resources upon this work. The decision is not wholly governed by the belief that it is the device most likely to contribute the greatest amount of health, wealth and happiness to mankind. On the contrary, the decision is quasi-military. If the world had settled into a true state of peace, the decision might have been made to use the available resources of men and materials for the exploration of a number of other discoveries which would have seemed of far greater promise.

So far as it is reasonable, chances of this type have been taken into account, but it is not sensible to state the decision which men will adopt when given a choice of two courses with the same precision as it is possible to know that a century hence the world will have developed new ways of producing food. In fact, the gloomy prophets of to-day who forecast world-wide starvation may seem as foolish as did Malthus in the nineteen thirties when surplus food was being destroyed. Those who speak of fuel shortage in the same way forget that we are certain to discover new ways of using fuel without the appalling waste now thought "inevitable." If men had devoted as much study to the working of their minds as to the working of their machines it might be easier to predict the future course of human conduct with the same confidence as we can watch the future course of material civilization. So, in the future, it may be that psychology and other so-called social sciences will use the scientific method and that in fifty years' time someone will be able to write a companion book devoted to what is bound to happen to human thought and action.

Little has been said of the great importance of this peering into the future. In the past there has been an enormous waste of effort and happiness through failure to look ahead. Lack of imagination, prejudice and sheer stupidity have been responsible, even more than selfishness, for human unhappiness and also particularly for the frustration of inventors upon whom, at least materially, so much depends. Yet a study of the future is essential if our modern plans are to succeed, if waste is to be avoided and if golden opportunities are to be taken. As a simple example, consider our roads. Fundamentally they are still roads that were made for 5 m.p.h. horse transport. To have foreseen the future at any time during the last hundred years would have saved not only thousands of millions of pounds but hundreds of thousands of deaths and injuries. Even to-day there is the danger of carriage-ways which are obsolete before they are completed because of our neglect to foresee the obvious.

In the early days of flying there were open spaces within reasonable distances of our cities and it would have been simple, if we had troubled to think, to reserve some of them for aerodromes. Now, at vast expense, we have to convert ground many miles from the centre of our cities. It is characteristic of our lack of foresight that we should be doing this just at the moment when it may seem that the future of short distance transport lies with the helicopter, which requires no great space in which to land.

Our houses are always built to meet our immediate needs; we often build them to last a hundred years without attempting to see the conditions that may exist in a mere twenty years. At the same time as we appoint a Royal Commission to inquire into ways of raising the birthrate we build houses that are apparently designed for families of not more than two children. The whole history of civilization since the industrial revolution has always been one of extemporisation.

By attempting to look ahead we can hope to control the future in the widest sense. By foreseeing dangers we can avoid them and by foreseeing possibilities we can take them in time to increase our wealth and happiness. In the chapters that follow are traced those events which are likely to happen during the next century. For reasons of convenience it is necessary to separate the subjects under headings, but it is important to remember that many of these developments will be simultaneous and, in some cases, alternative.

CHAPTER 1

THE DAWN OF THE ATOMIC AGE

WHEN in 1945 the world learned that atomic fission was a fact and that we had found out how to release some of the imprisoned energy of matter, there were bold forecasts that industry would be revolutionised. The problem of fuel, it was suggested, was solved for all time, since all matter is, theoretically, fissionable. We would be able to drive an 80,000 ton liner across the Atlantic on a small lump of coal, leave our lights burning all day and use power, costing next to nothing, for any and every purpose. The plentiful and unlimited power produced by atomic plants would greatly improve our standard of living and enable us to look forward to a twenty-hour working week.

To-day, a few years later, the picture is rather different, and it is widely realised that the development of atomic power for peace uses will be very much slower or more difficult than was supposed. During the war, everything was sacrificed to the production of the atomic bomb. Problems which could not be solved were by-passed wherever possible. The cost of results was no object. It has been stated that £500 million was spent before the production of the first atomic bomb, probably a greater sum than that spent on research in all industries during five years. The expenditure of this amount in three or four years was not the same thing as the use of less money over a greater period of years. Development and research were inevitably "lop-sided." Scientists had to go back, as it were, and begin again; in many cases trying to find out the why and wherefore of what they had already done. Normally, theoretical or "academic" research is in advance of practical application. In the case of the atom, because of the special circumstances, practical application had run ahead of theoretical research and there had to be a pause while the gap was bridged.

During the next few years scientists and technicians have to solve a number of problems, and not until these are decided can we look forward to the construction of industrial power plants based on atomic fission. Let us look at some of these difficulties and see how they might be conquered.

One of the problems is the development of materials that can withstand the tremendous temperatures involved in some of the processes. These materials must not only be able to bear temperature but must have certain structural qualities which remain unchanged when subjected over long periods to intense radio-activity. This is a technological problem which is likely to be overcome satisfactorily in a comparatively short time. In the last twenty years we have seen the successful solution of similar troubles in the motor industry. It is possible that the atomic age will call for materials hitherto of no particular importance, just as the production of aluminium made demands for the mineral cryolite which was previously of little interest.

Another problem lies in the disposal of the "ash" and other waste products from atomic plants. Up to now the world has produced the power it required by chemical reactions, generally burning or oxidation. The chemical change is accompanied by the generation of heat which is used, and the formation of new products which are partly discarded; ash, in the case of coal and wood, exhaust gases in the case of oil. The disposal of waste products involved problems no greater than those of transport and aesthetics, the latter generally ignored as our "dumps" reveal. The worst that happens if millions of cubic feet of impure carbon dioxide or even hydrocarbons from petrol or oil engines are poured into the air is a distasteful smell and possibly a slight headache for pedestrians. The passing of sulphur and carbon products into the air from coal fires and steam generators simply produces bad visibility, blackened lungs and the very slow destruction of building materials. But to dispose of the products of the atomic pile so carelessly might be to kill everyone within many miles. To allow even an ounce of the "ash" to escape would be dangerous because of its radio-activity. In any atomic plant it will be necessary to extract all radio-active particles from the "exhaust," the water used in the various processes and the "ash" obtained from the piles. Even with the experimental piles now in use this is a considerable problem. A complex "waterworks" is necessary to deal with the millions of gallons of effluent, dust extractors have to be used in all flues and air conditioning ducts. When the water and air have been made safe for release, there is still the radio-active material which, like the "ash" from the pile, may mean death for anyone in near contact.

The simple solution to the problem of disposal would

seem to be to bury the ash, throwing it into the sea is out of the question because of the widespread destruction of marine life that would take place and the dangers of the radio-activity being carried elsewhere. But the affair is not quite so simple after all. This radio-activity has often a "life" of a thousand years or more, and however carefully buried there is the possibility of it being accidentally uncovered to spread destruction at some future date. The problem is causing difficulties even now when the amount of discard from experimental plants can be measured in pounds. It will be very great when the ash is measured in tons for it must be remembered that it is intensively radio-active and there can be no question of transporting it on lorries or ships, certainly not without massive lead or other protective coverings. One futuristic solution might be found by packing the material periodically into a large rocket and firing it into space. Scattered at a height of several thousand miles, the radio-active material would be unlikely to do harm, but such would be the undesirable consequences of any highly radio-active dust entering the earth's atmosphere that even this method may be considered too dangerous. The rocket containing the waste would have to be designed to escape the earth's field of gravity or become a satellite, circling the earth at a distance of many thousands of miles. This question of "exhaust" products, incidentally, could become extremely important when advances make it possible to consider building a "space ship" propelled by atomic rockets. Uncontrolled use of atomic "fuels" might result in atmospheric poisoning and some international agreement not to use dangerous fuels within so many thousand miles of the earth would be essential.

All these difficulties we have considered are largely matters of technology and there is little doubt they will be overcome. More serious and fundamental from the point of view of industrial atomic power may prove the problem of the production of sufficient fuel to operate large atomic piles economically. At present the only primary fuel is the element Uranium 235 and reactors use only about 1-1,000th of the total uranium. Sir John Cockcroft has said that we can see the way to multiplying this factor by ten, but far greater efficiency would be required to support a world programme based on atomic fission. Theoretically, all atoms are fissionable, except those of helium, but the nuclei of most elements are so stable that they do not yet offer serious prospects as fuel. By a variation we might use hydrogen in fusion to helium, with the release of energy at a very high temperature. This is how the sun appears to produce its energy. But this is not yet a practical proposition because the "cycle" necessary is long and the requisite temperatures might only be obtainable by preliminary fission. The only commercial way we know to tap atomic energy is to use U 235 and this element occurs naturally in comparatively small amounts. The element is itself not common and most of it is in the form of U 238 which is not suitable for fission. The U 235 atoms occur in natural uranium only to the extent of about one part in a hundred and forty. An important part of any atomic fission plant is the separation of the U 235 atoms, an extremely elaborate business as they react chemically in the same way as the unwanted U 238 and the division has to be carried out by delicate physical apparatus. Unless more rich ores are found, it is difficult to envisage any wholesale construction of atomic power plants.

We shall probably get over this difficulty in the instance by the technique of "breeding" fuel. Without going into details, it can be said that the primary fuel U 235 can be burned in a reactor or pile so as to produce more "secondary fuel"—plutonium and thorium—than is consumed as primary fuel. Surplus neutrons are used for converting non-fissionable into fissionable atoms. This sounds like "getting something for nothing," but it is theoretically possible and practical research is already advanced. In the course of a few years it may be possible to build breeder-piles in which the fuel for industrial atomic plants will be produced, and instead of only about one-hundredth of the available energy of the uranium being used, it will all be available, such losses as might be experienced in practice being due to common engineering difficulties.

There is also the possibility that we shall be able to produce energy by the fission of other atoms. The prospect of being able to drive an Atlantic liner a thousand miles with a spoonful of water remains extremely unlikely, although the water undoubtedly contains the energy locked up, but there remains the hope that we shall discover how to employ the energy in elements other than uranium. The hydrogen bomb is suggestive of some success although it is infinitely easier to use a fusion of this nature for disruptive than for industrial purposes. At present it is sure that until we find a new way of obtaining fuel, the prospects of atomic plants contributing appreciably to the world's power sources remain remote, especially as a large proportion of the available fuel seems likely to be locked up in atomic weapons of destruction.

Atomic energy, if it is released in the pile without heat collection or in the atomic bomb disruptively, is not easy to use. We generally need it in the form of mechanical movement, electricity, or heat; some form in which we can control and distribute it as required. The assumption is that we must obtain it in the form of heat and for efficiency it must be at a high temperature. This raises new problems of engineering to devise means of transferring the heat in a form suitable to produce mechanical movement. To find a vehicle may not prove difficult. Sodium has been put forward as likely to meet the conditions, as it is not affected by intense radio-activity. But in the first instance the heat from atomic piles may be used for space heating rather than steam raising and we may expect the small towns arising round the experimental piles to be warmed by that method.

The real use of atomic energy will come when we discover some means of using the energy directly instead of indirectly. If we could convert this energy to electricity in one stage we should not only save waste but need far smaller generating stations. It must be admitted that the direct use of nuclear energy seems at the present time most difficult, but not perhaps more improbable than would a generating station appear to some of the eighteenth century physicists with their small battery-made currents lasting a few minutes at a time.

Compared with other forms of power generation or conversion an atomic plant will have difficulties which must be taken into account when considering the future of atomic energy. These may be summarised as great bulk and weight, potential danger and great cost in repair. The bulk and weight, as well as the risk, suggest that atomic energy will never be used directly for popular forms of transport. Size and weight are at present inevitable in any atomic power unit because a minimum "critical" weight of fuel and auxiliaries is required before the chain reaction will take place at all in any convertible manner. Just what this weight is may not now be published, but let it be imagined that this is no more than a few pounds, then added to this the weight and bulk of the apparatus required for turning the heat generated into mechanical motion and the weight of lead, concrete or other materials needed for protection against radio-activity or to control the pile, and it will be seen that questions of safety apart, the atomic car or motor cycle is unlikely to be seen in a lifetime. The minimum size and weight is still irreducible, a smaller unit would not give less power, but no power at all. This would seem to rule out the use of atomic power in most commercial aircraft as we know them to-day.

It is probable, however, that when large scale atomic power plants are established, some form of electricity storage more efficient than the accumulator may enable the power derived from nuclear fission to be used indirectly for transport. Given power, it is likely that inductive transmission without actual contact from sunken cables will be applied to some vehicles as in the case of small cranes and trucks now used in Russian factories. Even main roads could be electrified in this way. Shipping offers another special case, for the difficulties of weight and bulk need hardly apply. An atomic plant should occupy no more space than turbines or diesels and the weight of fuel would be saved. Theoretically 1 lb. of uranium gives the same energy as 7,000 tons of coal, sufficient to carry the largest Atlantic liner quite a long distance, and the use of such a plant has an obvious future for long term submarine warfare.

The question of safety is more complicated. Elaborate precautions have to be taken to ensure the health of workers in atomic plants. These include physical examinations, blood tests, the carrying of sensitive discs which show how much radiation has been encountered, protective clothing, and special handwashing. All this has been found necessary, in addition to many Geiger counters indicating the presence of radiation, the use of massive protective walls of concrete or lead and many other detail measures. Radio-activity is particularly dangerous because it gives no warning; there is no feeling, no taste, no smell and the radiation may be given off by an almost invisible piece of dust. The effects are often not immediate but culminative over a period; varying with the intensity of the radiation received, they can be extremely serious and can affect more than one generation.

Bearing in mind the elaborate precautions which have to be taken where professional workers, accustomed to discipline, are concerned, we can see the difficulty that would arise if any form of portable atomic "engine" could be designed. The "atomic car" might be made so that all exhaust gases, ashes or cooling water could be collected by skilled persons and any radio-active material screened so that it did not constitute a hazard to the driver or pass-ersby, but the risk of scattering as a result of an accident would be considered far too great. It is not the same risk as petrol; this may catch fire, but that is an open danger. Radio-active products might make the street unsafe for many years or have to be removed by elaborate and expensive processes. As a result of an accident the driver or other people might receive lethal doses of radio-activity before anything could be done.

We do not yet know all the physiological effects of radiation, the precautions taken in atomic plants are probably on the conservative side, the figures of "tolerance" being set rather low. On the other hand we have no experience of the eventual effects of very small doses of radiation over the course of years. We have set a limit to the amount of radiation that can be tolerated in water used for domestic purposes and suppose this to be "safe" because it does not cause any observable trouble. But we do not know what might be the result over several decades and it seems that too generous a use of tracer radio-active substances might cause mutations and that their use in quantity may be restricted to those who, medically, are persons over the age of reproduction. Our present knowledge does suggest, however, that the atom plants of the future may be kept well away from large centres of population and that those employed will have to be disciplined for their own safety. This for a time rules out the possibility of atomic plants being used for the propulsion of road vehicles or passenger aircraft, although there are already many indications that successful antidotes will be discovered to negative the effects of gamma rays other than for the longest periods of exposure.

An attachment to a radio set which can then indicate the presence of radiation is quite simple and it is worth noting that the danger of radiation will make the use of atomic fission as a peaceful explosive very difficult. The Russians have claimed to be "changing the face of the earth" with atomic explosives, but the danger of new deserts being produced cannot be ignored. Up to now we have devoted space to the explanation of what cannot be done and this may give the impression that there is no future for industrial power production by atomic fission. The indications are that it will be at least ten years before any useful power is produced in this way, except on an experimental scale and it may well be a century before there is any substantial "switch over" from coal, oil and water as our chief power sources. Indeed, the economics of atomic fission may make it necessary to reserve atomic plants for special projects that call for the use of power at points where natural fuels are scarce and the cost of transport prohibitive.

Having listed some of the possible handicaps of atomic power for industry, let us look at some of the advantages. There is, for instance, the enormous advantage of transport saved on fuel. Assuming the use of the present atomic "fuel," we have 1 lb. of uranium as equivalent in energy to 7,000 tons of coal. Transport of a mere ton of fuel a year would be sufficient to fuel a large plant, a matter of great importance for power plants in, say, Greenland or in the Australian desert. There are great engineering projects, such as the irrigation of waste land, which cannot be considered at present because of the cost and difficulty of transporting fuel to the power source. This difficulty disappears when atomic energy becomes available. The first great atomic plants are likely to be set up in remote parts of the earth, the older industrial centres continuing to obtain their power from coal, oil and hydro-electric stations.

Another important advantage is that the fuel will not call for a huge labour force engaged in unpleasant work. During the last few decades there has been increasing difficulty in persuading men to dig coal. The work is dirty, laborious and dangerous. A rising standard of living for workers in general is likely to increase the unpopularity of mining in inconvenient districts. Atomic industrial power may become available just in time to prevent a power famine due, not to exhaustion of coal reserves, but to the unwillingness of human beings to undertake the work. Underground gasification at present offers very little prospect of help. Uranium ores have to be mined, but if, as suggested, methods are found of using them effectively, the amount of labour will be comparatively small.

Yet another advantage of atomic power is that we eventually may be able to visualise its use on a gigantic scale, a scale not possible with our present methods of power production. In time such projects as the melting of polar ice may be undertaken with the object of adding thousands of square miles to the world's cultivated areas. It is on such plans, where cost is of relatively small importance, that atomic power may be used during the next hundred years. The economics of atomic fission as they appear to-day suggest that coal and oil have many years in front of them before they need fear serious competition from nuclear fission as a rival, always allowing for the discovery of better means for the storage or transmission of electricity. It is there that the wastage and maintenance charges are still so high that even our modern elementary knowledge can foresee a change.

Another good reason for believing that it is on special duties rather than for ordinary industrial and domestic use that atomic fission will be used is that the very great capital cost may not prove worth while in countries with plentiful supplies of coal, oil and water. Atomic power would be valuable only if it were cheaper, but this cheapness would not make so much difference as is sometimes supposed. The proportion of the cost of manufactured articles represented by the power used is no greater, on an average, than about one-eighth. In other words, halving the cost of the power will make possible a reduction of only about one-sixteenth in the price. Further, only a fraction of the cost of this power is represented by the normal cost of fuel. The rest is accounted for by distribution, repairs, and depreciation. It is not by atomic power applied to industry, therefore, that the people of the near future will see their twenty-hour working week. Or rather, atomic power will be only one of a number of factors that would make this possible.

To sum up: as a result of the "harnessing" of the atom during the next two decades we shall have experimental and "pilot" plants built for generating heat by atomic fission. These will be used to solve the great technical problems of materials, heat transfer, and waste disposal. At the same time research into fundamentals may show the way to produce nuclear "fuel" more efficiently and plentifully than by our present elaborate and expensive methods. The practicability of power generation by atomic fission having been demonstrated, plants are likely to be constructed at places in the world where power raising by other methods is impossible or uneconomical. We may reasonably anticipate that fifty years from now a number of large plants will actually be in operation and that "competition" between atomic power and power raised from coal or oil will have begun.

The facts and forecasts which are here set out may seem undramatic in comparison with those made when atomic fission was first announced. But they do not in the least detract from the great importance of atomic research. The generation of power is only one of the benefits that will come from atomic fission and although it is, after the simplicity of the uncontrolled bomb, the most discussed, it is not perhaps even the most important. Other developments may, indeed, make the use of atomic fission for power generation of secondary importance for the next hundred years, when it seems likely that there will remain ample supplies of our present sources of energy. We must consider also the increasing use of other stores of energy: tidal power, sun power, the heat of the earth itself or even wind power in new ways. Considerable technical progress has been made during the last twenty years in respect of all these methods. In every case they are practicable now and their development depends almost entirely upon improvements in maintenance, storage and power transmission.

Of the various sources of power, the direct use of the sun seems at first sight the most promising for immediate exploitation in that it does not seem to require any great capital expenditure. If we could successfully turn the energy of the sun which reaches us into another form of energy suitable for motive power, we should really be using atomic power, since the sun's energy is provided by atomic fusion. The net overall change of the solar energy cycle is the fusion of four hydrogen nuclei into one helium nucleus. This fusion results in a loss of mass amounting to 4,500,000 tons a second. Yet in a million years the sun loses only one per cent of its mass. Only a fraction of a millionth of this energy is intercepted in space by the earth, but nevertheless it averages about $1\frac{1}{2}$ h.p. per sq. yd. In other words, if we could collect and use all the sunshine falling on only four sq. yds. of the earth we should have sufficient energy to run a motor cycle. Hitherto, attempts have failed not because some of the energy could not be collected and used but because the loss due to inefficiency amounts to quite eighty-five per cent. It is necessary with modern devices to collect the sunshine from a vast area to obtain the equivalent of one h.p., and the ease with which this work is delivered by internal combustion engines renders the sun method far too cumbersome.

During the last ten years advances have been claimed particularly in Russia, where research has been stimulated by the existence of great areas, deficient in power supplies, but receiving abundant sunshine. (The Russians claim to be operating a canning factory in Tashkent with solar energy. In the United States plants have been built with an efficiency of fifteen per cent capable of cooking a meal and many Florida homes are provided with hot water by a closed cycle system in which the water is heated from a solar absorber on the roof. We may expect these devices to become common for water heating and even cooking in tropical countries where sunshine is abundant; after installation the fuel costs are nil. The heat is stored during the hours of darkness by keeping fluid in effectively insulated tanks; wet Glauber salts is one common medium for this purpose.)

All this, however, is far removed from using solar energy to provide industrial power and it is likely that large scale attempts to generate steam by aid of solar mirrors focused on a boiler are likely to fail because efficient steam generation requires a very high temperature. It is possible that within the next few years success may come from quite a different approach, the use of solar energy to generate electricity directly. So far we have made cells which produce but a fraction electrically of the energy of heat or light. If inventors succeed in devising cells able to absorb solar energy and convert it electrically with an efficiency of only thirty per cent we might expect factories in suitable sites to draw their power from their roofs. Deserts are usually places of abundant sunshine and we know that given ample power for irrigation many lands can be made fertile again.

Large scale attempts to harness the power of the tides have been much discussed, one of the greatest of all being

at Passamaquoddy Bay between Maine and New Bruns-
wick in North America, when the work was abandoned
halfway. Most of the problems concerned have now been
solved, including that of reducing the "dead" period when
the turbines could not run to a minimum. The chief difficulty is the tremendous capital expenditure required, but
there is little doubt that successful tidal generators could
have been built for a fraction of the sum expended on
atomic fission. Whether during the next century tidal
power is adopted on any great scale will depend, perhaps,
on whether a solution is found to the various problems
still involved in securing power from nuclear fission.

Wind power has largely been abandoned in the face of
competition from coal, oil, and water power, but new
knowledge of aero-dynamics has made it possible to design
wind-driven generators of much higher efficiency than the
old "windmills." A generator with blades sixty ft. long
supported on a tower over 200 ft. high was due for com-
pletion during 1950, to be erected in the Orkneys at a
spot where the average wind velocity is over fourteen
m.p.h. It is designed to produce one hundred kilowatts
and the great disadvantage of wind power—the "dead"
periods during which the wind velocity is insufficient to
generate power—will be overcome by feeding the electricity to the "grid," enabling steam-driven generators to
be "rested."

If this "pilot plant" is successful the plan is to install
groups of these wind-generators at suitable points which
have been indicated by wind velocity measurements round
the west coast of Britain. The cost of each major generator
would be £500,000 and a series of 500 would reduce the
coal bill of the "grid" by the cost of three million tons of
coal a year. It is anticipated that these generators could
supply about 10 per cent of the total power needs of
Britain.

The importance of this development may lie not only in

its contribution to Britain's power problem but in the possibilities it opens up of cheap power production in areas where neither coal nor water power is available. The Antarctic continent is notable for its high and constant winds and wind power generators may pave the way to the exploitation of the mineral wealth that is believed to lie under the ice and snow.

The great capital cost and overall inefficiency will possibly remain an obstacle to designs for securing power from the heat of the sea or from the earth itself. Detailed plans for such projects have been in existence for many years. Sir Charles Parsons produced plans for driving shafts into the earth in which steam would be generated by the heat of the interior of the earth and used to drive turbines. The cost of even a single installation might have to be reckoned in hundreds of millions of pounds. The further possibility that when the shafts were completed control of the heat at a distance of several miles would prove more difficult than anticipated may prove sufficient deterrent to further experiment for many years.

The determining factor in the development and use of all these sources of power, including atomic fission, will be the labour cost. Except for special purposes, atomic fission as we now know it may prove more expensive than coal or oil. On the other hand, the reserves of coal and oil in the world are not inexhaustible and in the far future it may be necessary to seek alternative sources, regardless of initial outlay. There is the increasingly important point to be borne in mind that it will become more and more difficult to persuade men to undertake the dangerous and unpleasant work of deep mining.

The picture of the world's power generation a century hence must be very different from that of to-day. Industries based on coal and requiring it as a raw material may be centred on new and more easily worked mines in places now quite undeveloped. It may be found necessary to con-

serve the world's dwindling supplies of oil for forms of
transport for which it is indispensable or to convert much
of our coal to oil by some system of hydrogenation.
Atomic power generators will be in operation in places
where power is essential for development but not obtainable from coal or water. There may be a great increase in
the number of comparatively small atomic units to produce power for local and domestic purposes. It will be
considered fantastic to burn coal, oil or wood in tropical
countries for heating water or cooling dwellings. Apart
from direct solar heat, more use will be made of the heat
pump which, working on a reversed refrigeration cycle,
can extract heat from a room to cool it or pump in heat
to warm it, requiring no other "fuel" than a supply of
water at a temperature different from that of the surround-
ing air. Such installations are already being used for buildings and swimming baths in Switzerland and are planned
for the space heating of buildings along the Thames.

A hundred years ago the production of coal in Britain
was comparatively small. In the United States it was
negligible. There was not a hydro-electric generator anywhere in the world. The changes in the next century are
not likely to be less marked. Coal may continue to be
used as a fuel for a period, but eventually it will be found
too valuable as a raw material for chemical industry and
for the production of coke for steel for it to be burned
wastefully for heat alone. There are signs already that
towns will not much longer tolerate the pouring into the
air of millions of tons of soot and acids as a result of burning "raw" coal; the open coal fire may well be forbidden
if its health value can be found in some more efficient substitute. The often forecast "oil famine" may be longer delayed than seems possible at the moment as a result of the
discovery of new sources of oil, improvements in methods
of extraction and a great increase in the efficiency with
which it is used. The production of "high octane" fuels

for internal combustion engines can theoretically be carried to the point where a gallon of spirit will drive an ordinary motor-car for 200 miles. Aircraft will increasingly use jet engines fed by heavier and cheaper liquid fuels and before supplies of natural oils become seriously restricted it is to be expected that internal combustion engines will be operating on synthetic fuels of much higher general efficiency.

These brief considerations of the future sources of power are necessary if atomic fission as a source of power is to be seen in true perspective. But it is certain that atomic research and the construction of plants for the production of radio-active materials would continue even if it appeared there was no hope for the economic generation of industrial power from atomic fission. The uses of the products of atomic plants may prove indeed so vital that atomic power will be relatively unimportant. First of all, fundamental research into the structure of matter will give us increasing control and may show the way to a whole series of new man-made materials. It is known that radio-activity can effect many chemical and physical changes; research in due course is sure to lead to the development of a large number of fundamentally novel manufacturing processes.

As a part of research, the products of atomic piles are already proving of immense importance. The atomic pile makes it possible to produce isotopes in sufficient quantities for research and the availability of these isotopes has given workers in every branch of science a new weapon that for its importance can only be compared to the invention of the microscope. The atoms of a given substance are not all the same. They behave chemically in exactly the same way, but the two or more different kinds of atoms differ in their structure. These different atoms are called isotopes, and if the isotope is radio-active it is called a radio-active isotope. These isotopes were known, of course, before atomic fission, the most notable instance being the isotope of hydrogen which is slightly heavier than "normal" hydrogen and in combination with oxygen gives "heavy water."

The value of radio-active isotopes in research lies in the way that individual atoms can be "labelled" and traced so easily. To take a simple example, we need phosphorus in our diet and take a certain amount in our food every day. This phosphorus finds its way to our bones, brain and other parts and some is eliminated. But it is only by the most elaborate dissections and analyses that we can piece together the story of what happens to the phosphorus between the moment when it is swallowed and the moment when it appears in the bones. Even then the story is incomplete; we cannot say, for instance, whether the phosphorus eliminated to-day was that eaten yesterday, the day before, or whether in fact it has come from some part of the body where it has been stored. If a minute amount of radio phosphorus is taken, it can be traced through the body by its radio-activity. Everywhere it goes it announces its presence and its exact movement can be watched electronically from the moment it enters the mouth to the moment, perhaps twenty-four hours later, when it lies in the teeth.

What is true of phosphorus is true of other elements and certain compounds. Isotopes provide the research worker with a reliable method of tracing the movements of individual atoms through any natural or artificial process. As the movement of the phosphorus in the body can be traced, so can the movement of, say, carbon and manganese atoms in a steel alloy. We apply fertiliser to the ground and eventually find it in plants. How does it get there? We have had only the haziest notions. Isotopes provide the opportunity of finding out exactly and thus gaining the knowledge of how to use fertilisers more efficiently. It may prove that we have been wasting a vast amount of ma-

terial and labour through the applications of substances to
the ground in the wrong form or at the wrong times.
Farmers can now detect the path of a beetle underground
or listen to ears of wheat with a Geiger counter to find
out how nourishment has been absorbed from the soil.

There is no branch of science in which these "tracers"
cannot yield knowledge of the greatest practical value.
They can help oil technologists to get a better understanding of friction, of which a reduction would mean a longer
"life" and greater efficiency in every engine. They can
help to reveal the secrets of strength in textiles, of the
properties of plastics. Their value in medicine is obvious
from the one example of phosphorus; in fifty years' time
we shall have a far more exact knowledge of the workings
of the human body and far more exact diagnoses. Brain
surgeons at the Massachusetts General Hospital in Boston
are using radio-active phosphorus to help locate brain
tumours. A far larger proportion of this tracer is absorbed
by tumours than by normal brain tissue.

It is difficult to exaggerate the effect that all this research
may have in twenty-five, fifty and a hundred years' time. It
opens out new possibilities in every industry. The most
far-reaching effects may come in connection with our food,
for isotopes may give the opportunity of mastering the
secret of plants and fungi which, by the aid of sunshine,
turn carbon, water and air into sugar so very much better
than we can do it ourselves.

The products of atomic piles also offer new weapons for
the treatment or location of disease. Radio-active isotopes
can be prepared with a limited "life" for a few days, after
a period their radio-activity is reduced and dies away.
This gives a method of carrying radio-activity to deep-
seated organs that could, perhaps, be operated upon or
successfully radiated. Radio-active iodine can be used in
this way to affect the thyroid, and many substances are
now important for treating various organs. This may

prove to be a system that has to be used with great caution because of other effects of the radio-activity, but there is no doubt that it will be increasingly employed. The atomic pile also provides us with an almost unlimited supply of radio-active materials which can be substituted for the rare and costly radium applied to the treatment of cancer. The intense beams of neutrons from an atomic pile can be used rather like X-rays to reveal the "invisible," such as the positions of atoms in a crystal or in metal. "Neutron Spectroscopy" will become an increasingly important tool in certain kinds of research.

A hundred years hence atomic fission will be a commonplace. People will be so used to radio-activity in its various forms that they will instinctively protect themselves against it when necessary. To-day we have millions of miles of potentially dangerous electric wires, with countless instruments and electrical appliances. Yet accidents are rare; we have grown up accustomed to take simple precautions such as avoiding "live" contacts, or switching off before adjusting any apparatus. All this would have seemed extremely dangerous to someone 150 years ago.

In the same way to-day we are apt to exaggerate the dangers of radio-activity. In a hundred years people will take atomic fission with all its potential dangers as much for granted as do we the motor-car or the aeroplane. The benefits they will have received are likely far to exceed any we have ourselves experienced from the great discoveries and inventions of the first half of the century. They may regard with pity and amusement the fact that nearly all the good things we possess to-day owed their true origin to one or another of so many wars.

CHAPTER 2

MACHINES WITHOUT MEN

HAVING examined how, in the future, power, which is the basis of every material advance in industrial civilisation, may be generated, we can now consider how the greatly increased power resources that will be available will be used. All power, however it is raised, is primarily intended to replace "man-power" in the crudest sense, to drive machines that will either do very much more work than the number of men required to operate them could accomplish unaided or to make the work more pleasant. Our present comparative prosperity which makes it possible to consider simultaneously a five-day week, a health service for everyone and a standard of life for the lowest

46

paid which, materially, is higher than that of the wealthy in bygone centuries, has been made possible not by replacing workers with machines but by increasing the output of each worker by the aid of machines. Development has been irregular. The use of machinery in building, for example, is relatively small and in motor-car manufacture it is relatively large. But in general the tendency is for power-operated machines to replace the muscles of workers.

To visualise the direction in which industry is going, we must consider briefly how it has evolved. The craftsman, working in his own home with his own tools, buying his own materials and selling his own products, slowly moved to the workshop. With a number of workmen co-operating, several advantages accrued. Each could specialise in certain operations, which meant that instead of spending nearly a lifetime mastering a craft, a man might become proficient in certain parts of it in a few years or even months. Specialisation brought with it large scale purchases by experts and introduced the salesmen who relieved the worker of his selling or distribution troubles. More particularly the workshop, which slowly became the factory, was soon able to use power other than that of human muscles. The home craftsman had no power available and it was not easy for him to build small water motors or windmills. With a number of workers, it was far more economical for the factory to supply power, first from water, later from coal.

The breaking down of comparatively complex processes into a series of simple operations is at the root of our speeding up of "consumer goods" production. It would have been quite impossible, 200 years ago, for a modern motor cycle to have been made because one metal worker in his lifetime could hardly have mastered the techniques of working in all the steels and other alloys used. To-day, motor cycle engines are made in hundreds by teams of which no single member is capable of producing the whole. Because construction is divided into the manufacture of separate parts and the assembly of these parts, an engine can be made by men and women who have little knowledge of internal combustion engines, steel alloys, the crystalline structure of metals and the score of other subjects that would have to be understood by a craftsman attempting single-handed to make an engine from the raw materials.

The tendency has been for the machines used in manufacture to become more and more complex and the tasks to be performed by human beings to become simpler in the sense of requiring less specialised skill or judgment. It may not be necessary for an individual worker to make even one part. His task may be limited to removing a piece of metal from a casting and passing it unfinished to another worker, or polishing a metal face. Thus is built up the mass production line that results in something so complex as a complete motor cycle. The next stage we are entering will be to design machines to perform all simple actions and to eliminate handwork altogether. The factory of the future will not boast of the number of men and women employed, but of the number *not* employed. The time is bound to come when factories are places where machines do the work and are even supervised by other machines, the work of human beings being limited to seeing that the control machines do their work correctly.

We have a foretaste of the future in a plant which makes radio sets almost entirely without handwork. This factory employs fifty people and makes as many wireless receivers as the normal factory with 1,500 hands. The workshops look different; instead of rows of men and women at work before machines or at benches, there is a line of steel-enclosed devices with just an odd supervisor here and there. This type of machine is known as "Electric Circuit making Equipment" and it produces wireless receivers complete with everything except valves. The processes carried out by the different units, entirely without human intervention, include shot-blasting, milling, metal coating, lacquering and circuit testing.

An ingenious idea makes it possible for processes, simple compared to those in orthodox factories, to result in a wired circuit. Plastic panels are moulded with depressions in carefully arranged positions. These panels are covered with metal by a spray. The metal is, of course, deposited thicker in the depressions and the panels are then milled, removing the metal everywhere except in the channels. Conduits are arranged so that they now give the equivalent of a wire embedded in the plastic, or of a coil, a condenser or a resistance. All this work is carried out by electrically controlled apparatus and at the end of the assembly line the whole circuit and every individual component is automatically tested. In practice a mistake in wiring cannot take place except by failure of one of the machines. Faults are very rare indeed.

One of these automatic assembly lines can turn out a set every two seconds. The cost varies considerably with the number being made but, assuming the assembly line is fully employed, it is about £2 a unit compared with four times that amount for sets built in the orthodox manner. A point to note is that the product, although a wireless receiver of good efficiency, is quite different in conception from the orthodox type. The designers have begun again from the beginning. When radio construction moved from the craftsman-workshop or laboratory to the factory, no fundamental changes took place, wire was accepted as the material for circuits. This has been broadly the case in all products when mass produced, machines were designed to carry out the same actions as the craftsman, and often with the same materials. Now we are beginning to look at the problem from another aspect, that of the machines alone. We have machines that can perform certain operations; how can the manufacture of this article be modified so that machines can carry it out? It may take us many years to get rid of our preconceived notions of manufacture just as we clung to the idea that a motor-car was a "horseless carriage" and should therefore be shaped like a carriage without the horse.

The automatic radio factory is unusual and there are obvious limitations to the sale of products intended chiefly for the millions who cannot afford a more elaborate set. But this system definitely points the way to the future when electronic devices will take the place of human beings at the work-bench. The factory of the future will be as different from that of to-day as is a modern hydro-electric generating station from a gasworks. The most striking feature of manufacturing in A.D. 2050 will be the absence of human beings. On your conducted tour of a factory a hundred years hence you might pass through "shop" after "shop" and see only a man and a woman here or there at a desk, facing dials and occasionally moving controls. Probably they will not even look harassed, knowing that the new electrical machine minders will give them due warning when attention is required.

The revolution in factories will be based on the use of machines. We will call them machines although they look more like wireless receivers or radar sets than the collection of wheels, cogs, cams, and levers generally associated with machinery which can complete every kind of manipulation faster and more accurately than human beings. The great advantage of the machine is that it never tires. Its accuracy may depend to a degree on wear, but this can be calculated in advance and allowed for in a way quite impossible in the case of a human being. The output of a machine and its reliability is not dependent on incalculable things such as a mother-in-law, a sick wife and child or a difficult journey to work, all of which can ruin the human operative.

Just as before the coming of the steam locomotive we

had its associated parts, the wheels, cogs, levers, cylinders and pistons, so to-day we have the "parts" of the electronic apparatus which will run the factory of the future. An important branch of invention will be largely a matter of improving, modifying and fitting them together. One of the modern worker's most vital organs is his eyes. The new machine has been given eyes through the photo-electric cell in its various forms. In the photo-electric cell changes in the light produce minute electrical changes which can be amplified and made to control very much greater electrical currents. One very simple application is in a restaurant where the shadow of a person approaching a service door produces changes in the photo-electric cell which result in the door opening without being touched. Another elementary use is in counting articles passing along a conveyor belt, each break of the light is registered by the photo-electric cell and is registered on a meter. But the photo-electric cell or combinations of cells can be used more elaborately, as in television where its ability to "see" almost equals that of the human eye.

A whole series of electronic devices is based on the possibility of small changes in electrical resistance being registered visually as a line or pattern on a cathode ray tube. The next step is to have a photo-electric cell "watching" the cathode ray tube and action can then be taken automatically as a result of the pattern that appears. Switchgear can also be operated instantaneously or delayed to any extent at the designer's will.

Now consider another type of simple electrical device. If a series of cards is punched with a hole, varying the position of the hole, and the cards are then passed over a series of "contacts," we can arrange a simple sorting device. When contact is made with a hole in position A, the card is dropped into one container, when contact is made through hole B, it falls into another container and so on. In fact, this is the method used for sorting the millions of postal orders cashed every week and it was only recording and sorting devices of this type that made it possible during the war to keep check upon our huge armies. If the authorities wanted to find one thousand men, completely fit, able to speak Arabic and with a knowledge of internal combustion engines, for example, they had only to pass many thousands of report cards through an appropriately set machine for the number of required men to be picked out.

This machine is increasingly used in business. What it amounts to is the use of electricity instead of words. It is apparatus of this kind, rolls of paper like those used in a pianola, cards or other convenient forms, which will be "machine minders" in the future factory. Instead of issuing a blue-print or instructions to the workman, a master record will be punched. The holes will be meaningless to a human being, but in the electronic equipment these may be equivalent to instructions to cut a piece of metal to certain dimensions, then remove a groove a sixteenth of an inch deep, drill four holes at specified points, remove surplus metal and polish the whole before passing it to the next machine.

The basic problem of the entirely automatic factory is to combine three types of device so as to obtain the desired results. The first type is the machine that is able to receive information and to act upon it. We have mentioned photo-electric cells and punched cards or paper rolls. But there are many other methods. The magnetic and acoustic mines are examples of receiving and acting upon information as to changes in magnetic field or the position and volume of a sound. We have the knowledge to-day to devise instruments that will act on any sort of information, a change in colour, temperature, chemical analysis, any kind of change can be registered and made to bring into operation a device of the second class. These will control the power of the actual tools, start the sand blast, drill, cutting edge or whatever it may be and stop it when required. The third class of machines are the actual tools which have already become extremely ingenious and are extensively used for production for every industry. Machines can make cigarettes and pack them, test the soldering on a tin of beef, sort the cards and working hours of a huge factory or assemble the parts of a clock, all with equal ease.

The first great step towards the factory of the future will come when the design of units of each of these three classes can be made fully adaptable. One reason there are not many full-automatic factories is that all the devices for it would have to be specially made for one special job so that when the "run" was finished, the machines would need to be scrapped. The human workman, however slow, can quite easily learn a new task, but for the most part the automatic devices we have to-day, especially in the third category, are designed for one job and no other. Now scientists are experimenting with various holding and moving machines that virtually reproduce the movements of the human arm, so that each can be adaptable to different sizes, shapes and movements. This plant would be controlled by the "information" unit which would perform the right movements at the right moments.

Controlling a whole series of these units will be a master unit which will dictate the necessary assembly, the testing of the finished article and perhaps its final packing. The size and complexity of this master control will naturally vary with the nature of the article under production. To manufacture a motor-car complete from the raw materials by automatic control, a not impossible achievement even with our present knowledge, will require an electronic control as complicated as the much publicised "electronic brains" which perform abstruse mathematical calculations. These large outfits which calculate and control in accordance with the "data" supplied to them are extremely costly, one reason why no attempt to construct an entirely automatic car factory, for example, is as yet considered. It is cheaper to use human beings. But this will change.

No doubt a ship owner offered a gyroscopic compass or automatic helmsman a century ago would have considered them as dangerous toys, far too delicate and expensive to be practicable on a ship. Yet to-day they are widely used. An automatic pilot for an aircraft would have seemed fantastic to the Wright brothers at the beginning of the century; it has taken less than half a century for them to become commonplace, with human pilots leaving them in complete charge of an aeroplane in flight for hours at a time.

If we are to enjoy the much higher standard of life generally anticipated, it can only arrive by more work. A higher standard of life and more work seems a contradiction in terms, unless we make the machines our slaves. Electronics offers this great possibility. We can adapt the saying about "making two blades of grass grow where only one had grown before." Electronics will make it possible for one man to make a hundred units where before he only made ten.

To a great extent we already have the means and the reason why this revolution in industry is likely to be comparatively slow is because of the so-called capital investment that must be made. A great deal of labour and material must be put into the construction of the new factories before they can produce anything at all; this implies doing without now to get a little more presently. If it were decided to invest in electronic factories at almost any cost, as it was agreed during the war to invest in atomic fission, we could probably have them in five years. Incidentally, it is worth noting now that because many of the processes are dangerous for human beings, atomic plants are to a high degree automatic in spite of their complexity. At Oak Ridge there are probably only about twenty human operators to the mile in ten miles of the instrument panels which are centrally controlled. According to reports the American atom plants use some 14,000 wholly automatic devices performing tasks that would otherwise be carried out with human hands. Any man-power shortage resulting from world war would bring great encouragement to progress in automatic factories.

Perhaps it is fortunate that we shall have evolution rather than revolution, for undoubtedly doubling or trebling our production would throw our clumsy economic system out of gear and cause "unemployment" which might end in direct sabotage of the factories or indirect sabotage by foolishly insisting that ten men should be paid for standing and watching a machine that required no supervision at all. To build a concrete road with mixing undertaken by means of teaspoons would give employment. But it is inherently wrong for human beings to do any work of this nature when machines can free them for better living.

The coming of the "automatic worker" has been foreseen for a considerable time; twenty years ago thoughtless people were seriously disturbed as to the possibility of "robots" taking control. There is not, of course, the slightest possibility of this in anything but the symbolical sense. The popular conception of the "robot" until a few years ago was a kind of articulated iron man which walked jerkily, could do anything that a human being could do, but lacked "soul." This led to many works of fiction in which the robots turned on their creators. The power that worked these robots was never very clear, and this is the vital point, for obviously it would have been possible for a mere child to pull a switch and by cutting off their motive force turn any "robot" in the world into so much useless metal. In fact, the "threat" of this kind of robot was never taken seriously by intelligent people, other than in the philosophical sense.

But the construction of ENIAC, the Electronic Numerical Integrator and Computor, and other elaborate electronic calculating devices, revived interest in the future "danger" of the robot, chiefly by the announcement that these devices had "memories" and could "think." To dismiss once and for all this threat of robot rule which might prejudice the development of automatic factories, we must think clearly what they are. The electronic calculator is only a more delicate instrument for carrying out the same things as the ordinary mechanical calculator used in thousands of offices. Instead of metal cogs it uses small electric charges to represent numbers. Instead of cams for manipulation, it has condensers and instead of levers or axles it has connecting wires. Until it is "told" to do something, it is just so many miles of wire and hundreds of electronic tubes. True, it can "exercise judgment," that is to say, when there are alternatives, decide without human intervention which alternatives to take, and it is this possibility that has created some alarm. But it can only exercise this judgment in a way which has been predetermined by its human operator. All its thinking is, as it were, "second class." The machine is quite incapable of producing an answer which has not been demanded. The idea that, if placed in control of a factory, it could decide to turn out aeroplanes instead of motor-cars would be too ludicrous to consider if it had not been seriously advanced.

The "memory" which fascinates many people is no more than the electrical equivalent of an indexed book. Far from needing to be feared, this "memory" will be of immense value, producing all relevant information, in the scientific sense, at the touch of a button. We can imagine at sometime in the future a central "library" consisting of an electronic memory to which all new data would be fed and from which information could be obtained. It is possible that by sometimes showing the association between a new discovery and an old, the electronic brain would from time to time solve difficult problems or even suggest new inventions. But it can never by itself obtain original data of any kind.

The comparison between electronic calculators and the human brain has been unfortunate. Their purposes are quite different. The electronic calculator is designed to undertake certain specific tasks and it may well carry them out very much more efficiently and faster than the human brain. The human brain is designed to "think"; to store, reproduce and associate information of all kinds. Its task is tremendous and it is almost miraculously complex; it contains an estimated 10,000 million nerve cells with functions which might be compared to the relays of the electronic calculator. They are more efficient than relays in the sense that they require only a minute fraction of the energy to operate them, but they are slower, perhaps a thousand times as slow. A single electronic calculator or "brain," to compare with a human brain in the simplest sense, would require a building several times as large as an aeroplane hangar to house it and the power of Niagara to work it for a few minutes.

The function of these calculators is clear and their future obvious. Their purpose is to release the much superior human true brain from uncreative and tedious work. There is nothing that ENIAC can do that could not be done by a trained mathematician, given time. The importance of the machine lies not only in saving a useful brain from months, perhaps years, of monotonous work but in saving time. The result might be so long in coming, with unaided human effort, that it would have lost its value. A striking example of this is in the calculators or "predictors" which determine the correct point at which to send a shell in order to make it meet an aeroplane flying at a considerable speed. The prediction could be worked out equally accurately by a man, but because he would be a thousand times slower and subject to fatigue,

by the time it was ready the result would be useless and
the aeroplane far out of sight.

It is not only in factories that electronic devices of various kinds will greatly increase output. They have already
been installed in many offices and without them the present trend towards centralisation of control in all kinds of
government and business would be impossible. Imagine
trying to sort by hand the million or so postal orders which
are constantly handled in Britain. Modern government
depends upon figures, the gathering, sorting and analysing
of thousands of groups of figures. This could be done by
a vast army of clerks; but the results would take so long
that they would have lost most of their value by the time
they were complete.

This was the case with the ten years' census, the detailed
analyses were not available before such changes had taken
place that the figures had become obsolete. If the trend
towards the "welfare state" continues we must expect the
installation of batteries of electronic devices which will
give the answer to every kind of question related to our
social life. They would be immensely valuable at an elec-
tion and could produce the count in a few minutes.

At present an appalling waste of man-power takes place
in the distributive trades and "services." Thousands of
intelligent men are engaged in collecting pennies on transport vehicles, punching tickets, opening and shutting
doors. As it is clear, however, that human beings will always demand a higher standard of living and that this can
come only by lowering the cost of such things as transport,
distribution and other services, we must expect to see increasing use made of machines to take the place of men.
New York's subways are already "mechanised" to the extent of requiring fewer trainmen and no ticket issuers. It
will in time, perhaps, be entirely mechanised with self-
driven trains controlled from a single point. The
"mechanical" conductor on the buses will begin with

ticket-issuing machines or the driver in control of the door admitting passengers as has already been tried in a few districts but without the driver being offered any "electronic assistants."

The earliest and greatest change is likely to occur in shops. At the present moment some hundreds of thousands of intelligent young men and women are employed in handing out packages and taking money. Their wages add appreciably to the cost of the articles, and their work is unproductive. So long as the wages they asked were a relative pittance, no one worried. But now that they ask, quite reasonably, why they should be paid less than other people, it becomes necessary to see how far their work can be replaced by machines. The "self-service" store is now a commonplace in the United States. It not only saves labour but the time of the shopper who simply walks round picking out what is required and then pays for it at the end of the tour. Surprisingly, the amount of "shoplifting" is much lower than in the usual shops.

The automatic shop will go much further. The shopper instead of going round the store and actually picking up packets of this and tins of that will merely mark a card. Handed in at the end of her round this will pass to an electronic machine which will interpret the marks in terms of the goods, release the required packages from chutes and present the ready-wrapped parcel. This would save the work of continually filling up shelves, work that requires considerable labour even in a self-service store. It would also make it possible for shops to remain open for much longer hours without hardship to the workers. One U.S. store already has a machine attached to its window which enables it virtually to remain open during the whole of the twenty-four hours. Any person passing who sees something they would like in the window inserts a coin, dictates his name and address, and the order is recorded for delivery as soon as the shop opens. It would be quite simple to extend this plan so that any article could be purchased and delivered. The "automatic" coin machine is limited in what it can supply, but an electrical device would make it simple to deliver any one of a hundred articles. The automatic garage which delivers the car when a number is dialled is already projected.

Only by using to the fullest the possibilities of machines in replacing men can we get both the high standard of living and the leisure that is now universally demanded. It is therefore somewhat ironical that the expression "full employment" should have come to mean that everyone is doing something rather than that everyone is fully employed in the sense of making the best use of his capacities. Yet it is only by fully employing everyone that high wages can be maintained, and employment must eventually mean asking for no labour which could be accomplished more easily or cheaply either by a machine or by a revision of accepted ideas. Consider an example of the kind of change we are to see. Proper use of machines can only be made and their great cost justified if they are fully used; this implies forgetting all "usual working hours" and assuming that a five-day week runs from Monday to Friday. We shall not be able to afford expensive and complex machines if their working hours are limited by those of the worker. There is nothing really new or revolutionary in this suggestion. "Railways" would not have "paid" if they had shut down except for the hours between 8 a.m. and 5 p.m. Twenty-four-hour working has been common in one or two industries such as steel and chemicals. Now it will spread to many other types of factories, and there is a technical as well as an economic reason for this assumption. The great disadvantage of continuous working was that machines would stand up to it for only limited periods. The metals of which they were made suffered from "fatigue." If the machines were worked continuously they failed.

In recent years tremendous progress has been made in conquering the problem of fatigue in metals. Improved alloys much more resistant to fatigue have been devised. Machines will still wear out and be liable to breakdown, but a more scientific approach to the problem makes it possible to forecast the breakdown and anticipate its effect. We have better ways of testing and have learned by experience how to design better machines; the aircraft industry, where the unexpected breakdown imposes such a terrible penalty, has made a great contribution from this point of view of which the benefits are only just beginning to be felt in other trades.

Another way in which the tremendous capital cost of plants with a high productivity per worker may be reduced is by forgetting old traditions and by revolutionising design. As an example, it is taken for granted that a "factory" is a building. The factory grew from the home workshop and it became more or less the rule that all plants must be enclosed in four walls and covered with a roof. But in the new factory, with the number of workers required to be protected from the weather comparatively few and working at only a few points, we can ask whether this expensive covering is really necessary. We have plenty of new metals and other materials which are resistant to weather. Already there are synthetic textile plants which have no "covering"; the containers, pipes and drums are all in the open. There is no more reason why they should be housed in an expensive structure than for putting a gasometer under a roof. The control rooms, naturally, are protected and the workers are as comfortable as in an old type of factory and far safer, since the absence of a building reduces fire and explosion hazards. It has been advances of this kind that have brought the cost of synthetic yarns down during recent years. There also has been good progress in the steel industry. In the latest plants one or two men in a comfortable control room are all that is needed to run a complete factory producing, for example, steel plates. Formerly a score of men would have had to feed the ingots, manage the furnaces and remove the finished output.

The chemical industry is also moving towards the automatic factory, using machines rather than men. The process of manufacture continues from unit to unit with no more than supervision. Control is exercised by "robots" and not human beings. An electrical device for keeping the temperature of a liquid in a tank at, say, 200 degrees will keep it there and not at 201 or at 199 as is almost certain in the case of the human controller, however skilled. The "wonder child" of the chemical industry is, perhaps, rayon, a substance almost unknown at the beginning of the century and even twenty years ago considered as a rather inferior substitute. Now it is the most widely used textile material in the world, after cotton. It is produced very largely by automatic devices, with the result that although quality has been improved very greatly the price has decreased to about one-eighth of that ruling thirty years ago. Rayon has always had to be "enterprising" because it was competing with natural products.

Mention of rayon suggests another way in which the factories of the future will be different. They will produce materials which do not exist to-day. Forty years ago the only "plastics" were bakelite and comparatively crude rayon. To-day there are many hundreds of plastics and no one would suggest that we are at the end of possibility. Plastics to-day can be, in fact, almost "made to measure." Instead of the scientist producing a new material and then looking round to see what can be done with it, he will be told that a material having certain specific characteristics is required and he will begin to make it without much delay. No material is "ideal" for a particular purpose. At best it is the most suitable of those available, taking into consideration many factors, including the cost. The research worker in the future will increasingly produce the "ideal" material, with particulars of weight, reinforcement, strength and appearance laid down beforehand. A new material may revolutionise a manufacturing process and one of the enormous advantages of plastics is the way many of them can be moulded in a single stage. It is possible to press out a finished article which, if metal or some other type of material had been used, would have required many different tools and the work of skilled men.

There are, perhaps, few really important natural raw materials yet to be discovered. But there is no end to the possibility of the synthesis of existing materials into new. We may succeed in producing plastics with the strength of steel and half its weight. Nylon has caused a revolution in the textile world, but other new plastics and methods of preparation may well be found. Plastic threads still have to be woven in any quantity. A new plastic which traps air like woven and knitted garments may be developed so that plastic cloth comparable with the old textiles could be produced without any weaving. It may even be possible to produce whole articles of shaped clothing without a single stitch. The raw materials will go into the machine one end and the vests and shirts come out at the other. If this sounds fantastic, consider for a moment what a woman of a hundred years ago would have said if you had shown her a nylon stocking and told her that they could be produced by the million for a few shillings each.

Many metals will be used in new forms. There is no theoretical limit to the number of alloys that can be devised and already to-day they are being made "to order." The designer tells the metallurgist what characteristics he needs and the metallurgist produces the alloy which may have quite "unnatural" properties, such as great strength at red heat or great hardness compared with lightness. Alloys have, of course, been made for many years, but it is only now that we are really coming to understand what happens to the molecules in an alloy. New research weapons, such as the X-ray spectrograph and radio-active isotopes, will increase our knowledge so that we can not only build new alloys with desirable properties but produce them very much more cheaply in quantity.

With new materials will come new methods of processing. (A hundred years ago if we wanted to make something hot we heated it by applying flames, hot gases, or some other method of heat transfer. To-day the heat can be produced electronically. The bar of metal or the cake to be cooked is placed in the electronic oven where it becomes hot, although its surroundings remain generally cold. Instead of the heat passing from the outside inwards, so that the temperature of different parts of the article being treated vary considerably, it is perfectly even throughout.) This means no cakes burned on the outside and raw inside and will, perhaps, be even more important in the heat treatment of metals or other materials. There is such complete control that a pie could be kept hot for hours without danger of being "dried up." Electronic heating or cooking is only one example of many new methods of processing just coming into use which will become commonplace in the next few decades and make possible the development of far more efficient factories.

We can use infra-red rays for drying and "stove enamelling" in a fraction of the time required by the older methods. One result is that in a production line there need be no hold up while newly painted parts are dried. Very high frequency sound waves are just beginning to be harnessed for various industrial processes. They make it possible to launder clothes by shaking the dirt out of fabric, without any of the usual rubbing with chemicals and water. They can be used to break up the fat particles in milk and produce "smoother" ice-cream. They can emulsify liquids that normally will not mix, such as oil and water, a process which may revolutionise machine lubrication. Ultrasonic waves can be used to produce substances in a very interesting colloidal form to give us more efficient fertilisers and new medicines, to mention only two possibilities out of many. Sound waves are even now being used in the testing and soldering of aluminium.

These are only a very few of the new methods of processing, now in their infancy, which will be widely developed in the near future. We are to-day spending more on scientific research than ever before, but the tendency will be to spend far larger sums; for it is beginning to be realised that a million pounds spent on research may in the course of ten years save a hundred or even a thousand millions.

Changes in factories will have their counterpart in the homes of the future. Large scale production makes the luxury of to-day the standard fitting of the home of to-morrow. Even now many of the homes of the poorest people have things such as refrigerators, drying cupboards, washing machines and radio diffusion which twenty years ago were found only in the possession of the wealthy. The housewife of to-morrow will have available all kinds of appliances which are still little more than laboratory curiosities. The dust and dirt which she spends so much of her time fighting will largely be eliminated by the disappearance of the coal fire. Coal will still have to be burned, perhaps, but "high frequency" waves will be used to make the particles deposit before they can escape into the open air. Rooms will be fitted with electronic dust collectors and any dust in the air will, as it approaches them, be attracted by the opposite electric charge and deposited. "Dusting" will mean periodical removal of the collected dust.

Electronic ovens make it easy to cook very much faster. A meal of roast meat and vegetables will be cooked in four or five minutes, and better cooked than by present methods. Stoves will be fitted with electronic devices that will "watch" the food and adjust the temperature to its appearance. In fact it is likely that much food will be prepared in factories and sold deep frozen to keep indefinitely in the refrigerator. Preparing a meal will be a matter of taking the plates from the refrigerator, placing them in the electronic oven for a minute or two to be thawed, heated, and then served. The paper-plastic plates will be thrown away, thus solving the problem of washing-up when in a hurry. It has even been suggested that soluble plastic plates could be made which, in very hot water, would dissolve and run down the drain.

Preparing food at home is one of the most wasteful and inefficient relics of the pre-industrial revolution days. Millions of hours a day are spent by housewives preparing meals with inefficient instruments because the amount to be made ready does not justify the installation of more elaborate machines. The tendency to-day is to consider that the remedy is what is called "communal feeding," but this is a passing phase. Communal feeding generally means dull and unimaginative food served in drab surroundings without privacy, whereas the majority of people prefer meals in their own home.

Factories which will, in effect, be very large scale restaurants, with the prepared dishes on plates being deep frozen and then sent to shops instead of served at tables, will make it possible for the housewife to have the advantage of large scale buying and preparation without the disadvantage of eating uncomfortably in public. No doubt these factories will employ highly skilled chefs as other factories employ highly paid designers. The food will be prepared under ideal hygienic conditions and much of the very dirty handling involved in the present system of distribution eliminated. Large scale production will make it possible to offer the choice of almost every conceivable dish.

The electronic processes which will revolutionise industry will also revolutionise the home, and make "servants" unnecessary. Internal television, for instance, may enable a mother to watch her baby in the bedroom above or the garden outside without having to move from her place in the sitting room. When the front door bell of the house of the future is rung, a picture of the visitor will be flashed on a screen and it will be simple to conduct a conversation or open the door without getting up. Rooms may be warmed by high-frequency currents so that the occupants could stand without any clothing, the window open, and yet feel perfectly warm. This could eliminate our rather crude and clumsy business of bedclothes. You could turn the high-frequency current to the desired temperature which would automatically be maintained during the night and clothes themselves may be electronically heated when we become unable to withstand the rigours of climate in the years before enclosed cities are properly developed.

These cases are quoted only as examples of the changes that are bound to come. It will not, after all, be so great a change as has occurred in the last forty years when between the Victorian house that required a dozen servants to run it and the modern flat which almost "runs itself" the difference is considered. No doubt there will always be housewives who prefer to use the broom and duster, just as there are women to-day who like to weave their own cloth on a handloom instead of buying from shops. But the woman of the future will demand complete freedom from the cares of "housework" and it is man's invention and industry that will make this possible.

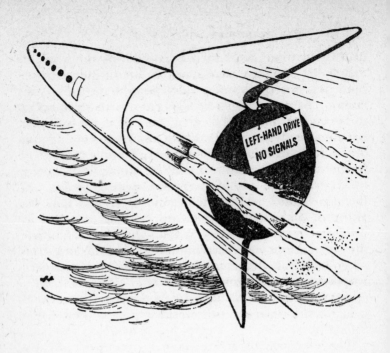

CHAPTER 3

TRANSPORT OF TO-MORROW

WE have glanced at future developments in the production of power and of machines that will be power-driven. But civilisation depends not only upon possessing the means to make things, but also the means to move them. The history of civilisation might, indeed, be described as the history of transport. This will be even more true to-morrow, although the present century has already seen advances in transport that equal all the progress made in every preceding century.

Consider that one hundred years ago the majority of men, except professional sailors, did not venture more

than twenty miles from their homes during the whole of
their lives. Railways were spreading in all industrialised
countries, but the average man never travelled in this
fashion. Now, one hundred years later, millions travel up
to twenty or thirty miles every day. Many thousands in
Britain alone travel every working day for fifty or one hundred miles. Millions own bicycles that enable them to go
further and faster than a stage coach could have carried
them and several million have motor-cars that can take
them in comfort two or three hundred miles a day. Sea
journeys which were still adventurous and generally un-
comfortable have become so tedious that even a four-day,
instead of a four-week, crossing has to be made endurable
by providing all the amenities of a luxury hotel on board.
Above all, aeroplanes have made inter-continental travel
a commonplace with ordinary commercial time-tables
bringing most places in the world within the travel time
of one week.

The exchange of goods between countries has been
revolutionised and transport has made possible the existence of industrial Britain; all our skill and enterprise in
industry would have been wasted if ships, aeroplanes,
trains and motor vehicles did not bring to us and distribute vast quantities of food. The large manufacturing
centres would cease to have life if transport did not allow
the daily migration of millions from their homes to factories, mines and offices. The future of transport is of
especial importance to Britain. What is it likely to be?

The future of land transport is virtually the future of
roads. Roads are still handicapped by the dimensional
limitations and mental "climate" of the horse-drawn vehicle. A far-seeing nation might have decided, when the
motor-car made its appearance, to leave the horse vehicle
roads to horses and build motor roads anew, as it built
railroads; the idea of running railways alongside the existing coach roads was rightly never considered.

No one seriously disputes that what is generally called "the road problem," the problem of accidents and delays, could be solved at a price. So far, the nation has never shown itself prepared to pay that price. Possibly a future generation, compelled by the alternatives of having safe and efficient roads or, for instance, raising the school age, may decide that it is better to have more children surviving to school leaving age than more children enjoying higher education.

Safe and efficient road transport is largely a matter of constructing roads designed for this purpose and of realising that as many of our present roads were primarily designed for traffic which moved at 4 m.p.h. they are basically incapable of meeting modern conditions. There is no excuse for building roads which must be useless in two years in an age when machines can take the place of fifty labourers and construct a surface almost as a carpet would be laid.

Pedestrians, horse vehicles and bicycles may be barred from the truck roads of the future. The flow of traffic and elimination of the overtaking which is responsible for so many accidents will perhaps be ensured by dividing the roads into lanes marked 30 m.p.h., 50 m.p.h., 60 m.p.h., with these speeds not only the maximum in the lanes, but also the approximate minimum. Crossings will all be "over or under." The motor-car will be regarded as a potentially dangerous vehicle, like the locomotive or aeroplane, and the idea of pedestrians walking across a traffic route will be compared with the straying of the jay-walkers on the railway or on the runways of aerodromes.

The motor-car itself will continue to develop very quickly, for it is far from efficient. It may not be long before the crudity of a mechanical gearbox is abolished. Introduction of the turbine instead of the reciprocating engine will also make for much smoother and more silent running. The development of cars has been strongly influenced by taxation and the elimination of this influence would permit progress upon better engineering principles. New fuels will make it possible to attain far greater efficiency. The 100 m.p.g. car is a reasonable expectation of the future and if the theoretical hopes of over 300 m.p.g. are never attained, it will be the ideal at which designers must aim. The motor-car still shows that it is descended from the "horseless carriage." Splash board design and front engines will one day disappear when all thought of "carriages" has been forgotten. During the next few decades there are unlikely to be many very revolutionary changes in cars; rather a steady process of evolution aimed at greater speed efficiency and comfort until the common car of 1990 will be as different from the models of to-day as our own are from those of 1920. Comfort is an increasingly important part of efficiency, so is convenience, and we may expect to see telephones on both cars and trains taken as a matter of course. Floodlighting for main roads, cars with small engines carried amidships and true independent springing are all possibilities of the future, as well as inductive pick-up for main roads, i.e., by burying coils just below the surface power might be transmitted to a pick-up device on vehicles without any material connection. This has already been attempted in certain Russian factories.

When the motor-car first became important, it was freely prophesied that the end of the railways was in sight. It was said at the beginning of the century that by 1950 all that would be left of the railways would be a few rusty mineral trains clanking about the countryside. Certain fundamental advantages of the railway were overlooked. For the conveyance of heavy loads it is far more efficient, but much of the "competition" of road vehicles has arisen from the fact that these can deliver from "door to door," whereas the railway is limited by its station. It is unlikely, therefore, that there will be any large scale railway construction in industrialised areas, but in countries which are being developed such as Africa and China, there must be many thousands of miles of railway track to be laid for heavy goods. The next fifty years may see railway construction on a considerable scale in Africa and Asia.

In most countries the tendency will be towards complete electrification for routes on which there is heavy traffic, with the advantages of service frequency, cleanliness and simplicity in operation. For goods traffic and long distance services there will be the development of diesel-electric and turbine locomotives of far greater power. It does not seem likely that there will be a general increase in speeds which are limited as much by the permanent way as by the locomotives. Long distance passenger traffic may eventually be completely suspended by competition from the air, but so long as the movement of coal, minerals and heavy goods of all kinds remains necessary it is likely that railways will continue to operate upon present day principles, the most notable changes being in the "cleaning up" of design, greater efficiency in locomotives and greater comfort in passenger coaches.

Sea transport will be even more influenced by the development of airways. It may only be the increasing number of people anxious to travel which will prevent passenger liners from being withdrawn during the next fifty years, although there is always the psychological argument that many of us do not travel only to arrive, but to enjoy the journey for its own sake. The one advantage that passenger liners will be able to offer over air travel is greater comfort, especially by the absence of vibration and noise. As aircraft become larger, with decks, saloons, cheap radiophones and even cinemas in the manner of luxury liners, this advantage will gradually disappear.

In the immediate future the notable development at sea is likely to be the application of gas turbines to marine work with the advantages of space saving and vibrationless running which apply to the steam turbine. Jet propulsion as developed for aircraft is unsuitable for marine engines because of the relatively low speeds required. The jet engine is inefficient at low speeds and an aircraft jet engine developing the equivalent of 10,000 h.p. at 400 m.p.h. would be far less effective at 40 knots, a reasonable speed at sea. Jet propulsion is therefore being adapted to the needs of ships through the medium of the gas turbine. Instead of direct reaction, the high speed turbine is geared down to the propellers and the problems which arise are largely mechanical—15,000 revolutions a minute is almost slow for the jet turbine, and to reduce this to a speed suitable for a ship's propeller demands the use of very specialised reduction gears. The problem of the turbine itself was very much that of finding alloys to withstand enormous stresses at high temperatures. These difficulties have been overcome in the main and very soon we may expect 40-knot passenger liners to be driven by gas turbines.

The tendency may be towards smaller liners and speeds will call for totally enclosed decks with air conditioned ventilation. Even the newest ships seem to bristle with "bits and pieces" like a 1910 motor-car. All these projections will be eliminated to lower air resistance which becomes so important at the higher speeds. A ship travelling at 40 m.p.h. into a 30 m.p.h. headwind uses a great deal of fuel to overcome air resistance alone. Ships of the aquaplane type are a distant possibility.

It will be many years before air transport seriously competes with ships for the carriage of heavy freight, although it will become economically more sound for certain types of goods to be carried by air. The Berlin air lift has been a revelation of the possibilities of air transport, although we must remember that at its best the great organisation only handled as much as two or three freighters and at any given moment there are thousands of freighters in all parts of the world. It is not until normal aircraft are capable of carrying loads of 100 tons and more that serious competition for the heavier and bulkier types of cargo will begin. The construction of much faster cargo ships, more efficient methods of loading and unloading and above all more efficient organisation so that expenses in warehousing and storage are reduced, will enable cargo ships to continue in competition with aircraft for quite fifty years.

The application of the jet principle to all forms of transport depends to a degree not generally appreciated upon the development of metal alloys capable of withstanding strain at high temperatures. The pressure on turbine blades may be in the order of many thousands of pounds to the square inch and the temperature exceeding that of nearly white-hot iron. Many new alloys are being developed to stand up to these conditions. Moreover these substances must have a long "life"; it may be possible to contemplate using military aircraft with an engine lasting a few hundred hours, but this is clearly impracticable for a locomotive or marine engine. Great progress has been made and alloys have now been developed with a life of 10,000 hours or more on the test bench under almost all known conditions of combustion temperature.

In the future we shall need quite new standards. The motorist in pioneer days expected to make repairs of some kind after nearly every journey. The motorist to-day asks for thousands of miles of trouble-free motoring and there are cars which travel 10,000 and even 20,000 miles without appreciable wear. We shall have the same advance in the case of jet engines, but the need to develop these special alloys means that progress may be slower than is often anticipated. The difficulty and delicacy of the work can be judged from the fact that the presence or absence of as little as one-thousandth part of one constituent in an alloy can make great differences in its properties, and these metals have to be produced, not on the laboratory scale, but by the hundredweight for forging into turbine blades and other components. Some of the latest applications of "carbide" and "fluorine" are leading to metals with greatly increased resistance to wear and to oils and tyres of such efficiency that cars may soon need no re-oiling during their life. Tyres running up to 100,000 miles are already being made.

The reciprocating internal combustion engine which has served heavier-than-air flying so well since its beginning is now on its way out and within fifty years of its large scale application to aviation it may be the exception rather than the rule. It has certain advantages for light planes which may result in its retention for a period, but the commercial and military aircraft of the future will be propelled by "jet" engines of various types. The older internal combustion engine is reaching the limits of its theoretical maximum power and jet propulsion enjoys certain other advantages which make it certain as the motive power of the future. There is a smaller number of moving parts, reduced vibration, safer fuel, the possibility of great power for weight, better streamlining and, above all, ability to fly in the stratosphere where the air is too "thin" for the ordinary airscrew. The advantage of very high altitude flights is, of course, that air resistance is reduced to a point where it is so low that enormous speeds are easy to attain.

In the immediate future there will be a considerable field for the prop-jet engine in which the fuel is burned as in the normal jet engine but the driving force is obtained, not from jet-reaction, but by gearing a turbine to propellers. Within ten years at least 500 m.p.h. should be the accepted average speed for commercial aviation using the turbo-jet engine. By that time considerable progress should have been made with the ram-jet engine which operates efficiently at higher speeds and which will eventually carry aircraft at well over 2,000 m.p.h. at high altitudes. True rocket propulsion will call for flights at a height of at least 100,000 ft. and will give us speeds of 5,000 m.p.h. and upwards with a present theoretical limit of about 18,000 m.p.h. for journeys near the earth and 25,000 m.p.h. for journeys in space. This would make possible the realisation of the ideal which has been suggested of an air service "anywhere in an hour on the hour," but it would be optimistic to suggest that the great problems involved will be solved in less than fifty years.

A much more immediate concern of aviation is the satisfactory solution of traffic control problems, likely to become more acute as the turbo-jet engine is increasingly used. The turbo-jet is only efficient at high speeds and it is impossible to contemplate jet-propelled commercial aircraft being "stacked" above an airfield, circling for minutes or even hours while waiting their turn to land. At present, thousands of flying hours a year are wasted by aircraft waiting in the air or being directed from one aerodrome to another because of weather conditions. An essential before real progress can be achieved is the development of completely safe landing systems which are independent of weather and of new methods of control so that far heavier traffic can be handled by aerodromes. There is no doubt that these systems will be introduced during the next decade and that aerodromes will work with the precision of railway termini and with landings in perfect safety every few seconds. The Berlin air lift alone has provided invaluable experience.

The question of control at airports, which has so lagged behind the development of traffic, can be solved by the co-operation of technician and organiser. The full and free development of air transport which is promised by technical discovery also calls for the elimination of much of the "red tape" which is a relic of the days when an intercontinental commercial flight was still something of a novelty. The nations will, in the near future, have to co-operate to simplify the whole business pattern which now threatens to bog civil aviation in a morass of forms and documents.

The greatest need for aviation in the near future is that of very greatly reduced operating costs so that flying becomes not a luxury but the usual method of passenger transport. There is hardly a country in the world which at the present time is not losing millions of pounds a year on its air lines, even with the present absurdly high fares. There are many reasons for this failure, but one is the great cost of developing the really large and efficient aircraft which are so essential to the establishment of civil aviation. Once these large aircraft, carrying one hundred passengers and upwards, are in full production, it should prove possible for fares to be reduced to the point where they are well below those for surface transport to-day.

One great adventure that awaits future generations is a flight through space to the moon. It has been suggested by some experts that such a flight should be possible within twenty-five years, but the figure is likely to be nearer a century. The problem of designing a space ship capable of making the journey has been solved on the drawing-board, but it is often forgotten that we should be exploring unknown territory and that experience is likely to reveal difficulties of which the very nature is at present beyond our ken. Columbus, when he set out on his great voyage, had, after all, the considerable knowledge of sea navigation accumulated during several hundred years. We know nothing of space navigation, and of what lies beyond about twenty miles of the earth's surface we are almost entirely ignorant. It is certain that conditions differ in many ways from those of which we have any first-hand experience, quite apart from the thinness of the air and other inferential data.

We know, for example, that there is what is called the "ozone layer" where much of the ultra-violet radiation from the sun is absorbed and in which the temperature is much higher than below. Above this layer intense radiation would have to be met, possibly radiation capable of blinding and killing. As we approach the limits of the atmosphere, does the composition of the air change, so that the familiar gases are mixed in different proportions? We do not know. Beyond is the ionosphere in which we believe, again by inference, that the air is so attenuated as to behave like the gas in a neon tube. It is here that the aurora appears and it is probable that the temperature is very high; estimates vary from boiling point to what would be the dull red heat of iron. Our knowledge of the ionosphere is limited, but it is fairly certain that any space ship passing through it would have to contend with high temperatures, possibly with cosmic rays producing unpredictable effects, and with meteors, the great majority of which, however, are safely consumed by friction as they approach the earth. There is evidence that the atmosphere extends to a height or distance of up to 600 miles and it is this region, perhaps, rather than the "space" beyond which will prove the most difficult to navigate. It is even suggested that comet-tail gases could be dangerous at vast distances from the earth.

These circumstances are mentioned merely to show that a thorough exploration of the atmosphere must precede any attempt to construct a space ship. Exploration will probably be carried out in the next ten years by means of instrument-carrying rockets. These projectiles will record temperatures and other conditions and take samples of air and photographs which will enable us slowly to accumulate sufficient knowledge to contemplate constructing a man-carrying ship capable of navigation. The exploratory work which has already begun will be comparatively undramatic and the picture that will be built up will interest experts rather than the public eagerly awaiting news of the first space ship. Nevertheless this preliminary work is very necessary, as essential to navigation as was the patient work of Harrison with the chronometer, although it was the explorers of new land who won the popular acclaim. Rockets will doubtless reach the moon, perhaps to return with "samples and soundings," long before man can make the journey.

The first rocket flights made by humans may be in projectiles resembling the V2 in appearance, but far larger. The "pilot" would require a sealed pressure cabin and, unless some means can be devised to secure the necessary acceleration very much more slowly than seems possible to-day, he will have some artificial aid like a "G-suit" to enable him to withstand the tremendous thrust of the poundage necessary to take him to 200 miles. The actual speed itself is of no importance physiologically. A man travelling at 2,000 m.p.h. suffers no more discomfort than at 200 m.p.h. and unless he has objects by which to judge, he is unaware of his speed. But acceleration is another matter. The acceleration of a V2 rocket would be sufficient to crush a man inside it unless some form of protection were provided. He would be thrust backwards and nearly flattened against the wall of his cabin. Gradual acceleration would be necessary for another reason. The initial speed required to "escape" the earth's gravity, something like seven miles a second, would cause friction in the atmosphere that could overheat any known metal or any alloy in prospect. It is probable, therefore, that projectiles will work in stages, with more powerful rockets to be cut in as speed is gained and the dense air left behind.

The first man-carrying rockets are likely to have detachable cabins so that when the atmosphere is reached on the return they can be released from the rocket and descend by parachute. The rocket projectile itself will attain a very high speed under the earth's gravity and if it is not destroyed by friction with the atmosphere or rocket controlled, it may be necessary to arrange for it to be destroyed before landing because of the danger to life and property. Flights of this kind might be made in far less time than a hundred years of waiting if expenditure upon warfare could be applied to a more interesting purpose.

With the problem of high speed flight through the upper atmosphere solved, engineers will be able to turn more seriously to the much-talked-of flight to the moon. In practice, it is likely that, except perhaps for experimental purposes, the moon will be neglected, for it is a "dead" land on which life would be extremely hard to support even if a successful landing were made. Space suits have already been designed for use by those who first attempt this great experiment.

Much more practical results will flow from the construction of space ships which, instead of seeking to escape the earth's gravitational pull, will make use of it to hold themselves in position so that they circle the earth, becoming, in fact, artificial satellites. The advantages of establishing these "platforms" are such that the possibility of construction is being examined by the U.S. Defense Department, and it is unofficially stated that results might be obtained in as short a time as ten years. The value of such platforms from a military point of view would be considerable; they might make it possible virtually to control radio communications on the earth. They would certainly make it easier to guide projectiles by radio with great accuracy and to observe the resulting explosions.

It has also been suggested that the sun's rays might be so focussed that they could serve as a "death ray," scorching any part of the earth desired. But the platforms would have other more practicable and important applications. Four space-houses established at a distance that would ensure rotations at exactly the same period as the earth would enable our world to be satisfactorily "covered" for radio. Signals might even be directed to the satellite and then "broadcast," solving the problem of long distance television communication. It is probable also that meteorological data obtained at this height would be of great value in accurate long distance weather forecasting.

The construction of a wireless transmitter on a space platform at first sight seems a hopeless task, but those who have interested themselves in the project say that sixty "rocket loads" of material would be sufficient and point out that there would be no need to construct a "platform." Because of the balance of the gravitational pulls between the earth and the moon it would only be necessary to "dump" the material to be sure of its being there at any future time; it would continue circling the earth for ever. Constructional engineers, provided they had suits capable of protecting them from the low temperature and absence of pressure, would be able to work without standing on any material thing; it is suggested that small cylinders containing gas under pressure could be used to "jet propel" them when they wished to move about. Nothing would fall because nothing would have any "weight."

Once the platforms were established, it is claimed that they would have to be spun to overcome this great difficulty of the absence of gravity. There are hopes that the difference between the zero temperature of space and the great heat of the sun's rays would provide the energy necessary for spinning the platforms and for working any electrical installations. The fascination of exploring in these regions is indicated by one fact. As the ultimate low temperature of absolute zero is approached, the conductivity of metals is greatly increased; a small electric current instead of rapidly disappearing in a copper wire would continue without appreciable "loss." This would obviously have profound effects upon radio installations in space. The properties of all matter changes at these low temperatures and the first space explorers will certainly be open to surprise. Once established, space platforms would be supplied by rockets from the earth and the time may come when young men enter the space platform service instead of our colonial administration.

The appeal of flight to another world will remain and the moon is as yet the only destination we can seriously consider in the foreseeable future. Even although it is true that when escape from the earth's gravitational pull had been made, the energy required to maintain a speed of many thousand miles an hour would be small, a journey to Mars which has been described so often in imagination would occupy 200 days, and the time to Jupiter would be nearly six years. These things are not "impossible," but any realistic view of the difficulties of a journey to the planets must put the time in centuries, rather than decades, from our lifetime.

On this subject of moon flight it seems that anticipation has outrun realisation; there are scores of experts who have worked out the necessary data, while others have designed space ships capable of making the trip. Although the flight might be possible, even with existing fuels, the major problem may be found to be that of passing through the atmosphere. For this purpose it will doubtless be necessary to construct the ship with a double hull, able to insulate the interior from the intense heat of the ionosphere and the cold of space. The surface will have to be highly polished to reflect the sun's rays; heat absorption in space would cause great difficulties, although a way may be found of utilising it to provide power for auxiliary machinery. A landing on the moon would call for special equipment such as heated suits, oxygen supplies and leaded asbestos to make walking feasible; the gravitational pull is only one-fifth that on the earth. In practice there would undoubtedly be other difficulties such as extremes of temperatures varying between that of hot water and 150 degrees below zero, and the deep dust in which the moon's surface is believed to be covered. Should this have contained uranium we could have expected exploration companies to be considered in the near future.

In time, all these difficulties will certainly be overcome, although not without vast expense and serious loss of life, for in spite of the confidence of planners and science fiction writers, there are many unknown quantities and there must be large numbers of crewless projectiles directed at the moon before any attempt is made with a manned space ship. The crewless vessel could be fitted with an explosive head, the ignition of which could be observed from the earth or it could be equipped with an automatic wireless transmitter to send back data of all kinds. Because of the problems of acceleration, pressure and temperature, a manned ship. will have to be very much more elaborate than a crewless projectile and only the insatiable desire of man to find out leads us to know that people in the future will not be content until the day arrives for personal exploration. With our present fuels and any in immediate prospect, projectiles and space ships would need to be very large indeed for even the smallest "pay load." The invention that will revolutionise this form of transport, when it is realised, is the harnessing of atomic energy in a suitable form. At present, such a solution is beyond our powers although, theoretically, three or four pounds of fuel would be sufficient for a journey to the moon.

Many years before the, to us, sensational days of space travel there will be a great advance in the general use of aircraft for ordinary business or pleasure purposes. New light alloys and especially fuel research may make practicable the flying car. Vehicles of this type have already been constructed but are inefficient on land and in the air on account of the high power required. Some kind of diesel-fuel motor might remedy this disadvantage in conjunction with the use of rocket fuel for very short flights. Under present-day conditions there is something absurd about a journey by road over crowded streets, solely be-

cause the car may be wanted at the end of the day. Tak-
ing-off points on main roads could be easily arranged and
at high air speeds a flight of ten minutes would enable
nearly all main traffic to be avoided round large cities.

There is no doubt that the tendencies of all travel are
wrapped up in the two main themes of more speed and
greater comfort. Within fifty years we shall regard the
crowded, noisy and often insanitary conditions of present-
day passenger transport as of historic interest, for transport of all kinds has changed steadily without any break
for many centuries. To be always in contact with home
or place of business will soon be an essential and the ideal
of many travellers will one day be accomplished in that
they will never know that they are travelling. The only
antidote to more and more travel lies in the ease with
which the sensations of sight or sound will soon be transmitted over the entire world.

CHAPTER 4

SPORT AND LEISURE IN THE FUTURE

THE object of all rapid transport and, indeed, of an *automation* abundance of "labour saving" materials and machines is to "save time." The cynic sometimes asks "to save time for what?" The criticism has some basis, for there is no purpose in "saving" an hour a day with the aid of machinery if we find "time on our hands" and suffer from boredom.) For this reason the peasant who, because of his inefficiency, has to work long hours and has no "spare time" often seems happier than the trade union craftsman who has secured a short working week and does not know what to do with himself when he is not working. Work could, perhaps, be defined as "doing something we do not want to do on someone else's time."

A great deal of trouble arises because of failure to appreciate that the distinction between "play" and "work" is almost wholly artificial. Digging a potato patch, the gardener's work which he protests he must not do for more than forty-four hours a week, becomes the bank clerk's play and sedentary workers may wish that they had time to spend in mending the garden fence. The only sensible distinction possible between work and play or leisure is that work is compulsory in exchange for pay, while leisure is the period in which you can do as you like, regardless of whether it is profitable or not. Work is what has to be done to earn the means of living and play is something you do to please yourself. The important difference is not what is done, but the object in doing it at all. To chase a small ball over miles of a golf course would be extremely hard work to some and it would give them as little pleasure to do it for forty hours a week as would the average golfer be happy to write a book or experiment in a laboratory.

Compulsion as to the form leisure takes turns it into work. A game of football is work for a professional footballer, he even has a trade union to see, not so much that he does not play too hard, as that he receives an adequate reward. Compulsory games are "work" for the schoolboy, although if he wants to play they can be as enjoyable as any kind of work. It is important to distinguish between pleasure and enjoyment and leisure or play, many of the world's hardest workers enjoying their working hours, far more, possibly, than their leisure. Confused ideas as to work and play have led to the conclusion that happiness is solely dependent upon a minimum of work.

Experience is showing that this is by no means necessarily true and the converse of the proposition is equally obvious. Unemployment is often feared for other than economic reasons; the unemployed man to-day may receive more money for "doing nothing" than his grandfather could earn by a week's hard work. Unemployment is feared because it provides a leisure that seemed attractive when doing uncongenial work but which proves even more tiresome than the work when experienced. The great fear of the past, and rightly, was overwork. The dread of to-day is insufficient work. Sociologists might find it fruitful to discover whether there is any connection between the figures for the increasing number of crimes, especially among the young, and the steadily falling number of hours a week worked during recent years.

This statement of some of the simpler principles involved in work and play is useful when considering the possible developments of the future. The habit and tradition of work, often of a very laborious and monotonous kind, is so deeply ingrained that we have been very much more successful in reducing working hours and providing more leisure than in learning what to do with the leisure. "Saving time" in one way or another has become a mania; we have been so busy "saving time" that we have not given sufficient consideration to what to do with the time bank. Like the miser who hoards gold we have considered that saving time was worth-while for its own sake whereas both commodities can only be valued in terms of what they can provide.

At present, the number of hours which the majority work every week is established by agreement or law and the tendency is for it to become smaller. Most people now spend only about one quarter of their time at work. There has never been a period when so many people had so much leisure, although in the United States men and women do not enjoy quite so much spare time because there they prefer to work a little longer to earn a "higher standard of living," in other words to get the things which they consider are necessary to make their leisure enjoyable.

This is a point which all highly organised countries will have to decide for themselves. Not how much leisure should the average man have, we know that approximately just as we know the minimum wage consistent with living in good health, but how much leisure does the average man want? It is a subject that has been little considered by unions and others who have concerned themselves mainly in protecting the ordinary man against economic exploitation.

Our hours of work could be halved to-morrow, giving every man another twenty odd hours of leisure a week. The price would be that of halving the number of things he could buy or, for that matter, which would be available. Some might consider this well worth-while. One of the happiest men the world has known is said to have been Diogenes who lived in a barrel and who could think of nothing he wanted from Alexander the Great except that he should get from between him and the sun. But philosophers of this kind are few and they are misfits in a highly organised society which rounds up its "tramps," makes having no visible means of support a crime, prizes the right to work not too long or hard very highly and even "directs" men and women to tasks which it considers useful to the community.

The need, therefore, is to draw up a "work and play" budget, a budget in which hours of work and leisure for the nation are balanced as money expenditure and revenue are balanced financially. The minister responsible would have to obtain estimates of the number of hours that must be worked to provide the goods and services necessary to maintain the standard of living. It would then be for him to "assess" the different industries with the hours of work required from them during the coming year, and these figures would, again, have to be broken down in terms of individuals. Hitherto, the number of hours worked has been a matter of bargaining, each side thinking itself better for more or less hours worked respectively. This will change as people realise that nations, like individual families, cannot spend more than they earn, indefinitely. There is another way in which it will be possible to reduce the hours worked; by increasing the productivity of each hour. But that does not alter the general proposition.

When the time comes for a budget of this kind there will be far more flexibility than at present. The capacity for work and the liking for work varies very greatly with the individual and, with the passing of the need for protective legislation, it may be as easy for the man who wants to work twice as long as the norm to do so as it will be for those who want to work half as long. The former may be one who cannot enjoy his leisure unless the entertainment is provided by others; he must go frequently to theatres, cinemas, horse racing, football matches or whatever it may be. With a forty-four-hour week his share may not give him sufficient to buy these pleasures and he would be happy working another ten in the week in order to enjoy the remaining 114 hours in his own way.

There is another type who spends his leisure creatively or contemplatively and who would prefer to earn a little less and have more time. It is as fantastic to forbid anyone to work too hard or too long as it is to forbid them to work too little. Indeed there is a real danger in the near future of the "organisation" of leisure and it is possible to catch a weird but not absurd glimpse of a future in which drab men are marshalled into dreary sports grounds to have their compulsory entertainment. The wheel will have turned full circle from a century ago when human beings were driven by economic pressure to work in unhealthy factories for most of their waking lives. If we seek an age of leisure with the ideas and attitudes of an age of "work," the great majority of people will have much time to spend away from work but little leisure and enjoyment. They will feel as frustrated and exhausted by their play as formerly by their work. Leisure is still far too novel a thing for the majority to be able to distinguish it from sheer reckless pleasure.

True leisure is very difficult to secure when the proportion of time that has to be given to secure the mere necessities of living is so great. Shopping, transport, form-filling and housekeeping absorb a tremendous amount of energy. The paradox is that the greater the amount of rest demanded, the more of that leisure is absorbed in these tasks. Because shop assistants demand fewer working hours, shopping becomes more difficult for everyone else and, for that matter, the shop assistant herself. Domestic helps of all kinds demand higher payment and shorter hours. This means that others must do more and therefore enjoy less genuine rest. One man's peace must always mean another's work to a greater or lesser degree, and the only possible way in which deflected work can be reduced is by the increasing use of "labour saving" devices and the development of such machinery for rest-time pursuits is no less important than for productive industry.

This paradox is likely to cause acute difficulties unless resolved in connection with the "long week-end" which is now generally accepted. Certain classes of people who have to work on Saturday afternoons or Sundays have revolted, asking why they should work when everyone else is on holiday. Yet in the case of transport and hotel and restaurant workers, and many other groups, unless they are on duty when others are resting, no one can take a holiday other than by sitting in his own home. Up to now the principle has been to raise the rate of pay to make the "out of hours" work more acceptable, but in the future something more will be required. Perhaps we shall have to revolutionise our ideas that certain hours and certain days are "usual" for working while others are natural holidays. The "five-day" week might consist of any consecutive five days and not necessarily the five days from Monday to

Friday. A seven-hour day might mean any consecutive seven hours. Clearly there are difficulties, because various industries and services have to co-ordinate, but these details can be overcome once the idea is accepted.

It may well be that when the whole question is examined, it will be found there are many people who would prefer to work a six-, seven- or even eight-day "week" if this would enable them to earn the same amount in twelve months, but allow for six weeks' holiday or more instead of the accepted fortnight. There is much that could be done in a "long" holiday of this kind that would be impracticable on thirty or forty Saturdays. One of the reasons why people belonging to certain professions, such as teaching, the law and the Church, have been able to make notable contributions to the arts and sciences is that they have had so much consecutive leisure.

It should now be possible for a very much greater number of men and women to join in the search for knowledge of all kinds. This is the age of the specialist, the "planned" discovery or invention in the laboratory as highly organised as a government office. But major discoveries in every field will continue to be made by the lone worker. Even in highly technical spheres there are great opportunities for spare time research, provided the individual has the time, and it is noteworthy that very few great inventions have ever come from the communal type of workshop or from officially organised laboratories.

In the higher positions of teaching, the lecturer has never been expected to devote the major part of his time to teaching. He is deliberately given opportunity for research and creative work which bring credit to the university to which he is attached. In an age of leisure we should see a great extension of this idea. The number of people who, given the time and facilities, would be able to do original work is very considerable. This field has been seriously neglected by "authority." The idea seems to be "adult education," the cramming of more so-called facts and second-hand knowledge into memories. This has its small uses, but (the future may bring us "public laboratories" as well accepted as public libraries. The provision of places where people can spend their time creatively in the sciences and arts is no less important than the setting aside of playing fields where bodies can be exercised.)

The ordinary man who works in a factory for forty hours a week is not expected to discover miraculous drugs during his leisure hours, although this is quite possible. One great field for the "amateur" is in the social sciences which are in many cases not sciences at all because the amount of speculation is so large compared with the very modest amount of observed information. It is just in providing this fundamental information that the amateur can help. The realms of zoology, geology and botany as they were born owed an immense amount to the work of enthusiasts, and social investigations which are concerned with the common people should encourage the more intelligent to work creatively.

All these changes are very probable, for (up to now our idea of "creative" leisure has been limited, with far too much emphasis on the passive side; learning to appreciate music, literature and painting instead of making them; learning to weave baskets, or cook standard dishes rather than to create something new. Without a very strong growth of the element of novelty in leisure there will be a growing sense of boredom and restlessness that will find its outlet in crime, obsession with professional sports and spectacle, even a secret longing for the "good old days" when a man worked forty-eight hours a week and did not have to worry about having "nothing original to do" in his spare time.)

Sport will almost certainly become more important. It will inevitably become more scientifically technical, more mechanised and less a matter of chance. Every possible scientific discovery of recent years has been adapted to the purpose of removing the element of chance from sports. Chronographs tested at the National Physical Laboratory have been introduced and then superseded because, even with this apparatus correct to a tenth of a second, it is possible to have an error of the human element by mis-judging the moment involved. The consequence is seen in the "photo-finish" in its various forms, capable of sepa-rating runners, human, canine or equine, by a "nose" and giving the time to a hundredth of a second. It is interest-ing to note that the various devices used to-day in athletics have been taken from the "scientific sports"; electrical timing strips, photo-finishes and automatic starting were all introduced by motor racing and aviation.

The part played by science in judging sport was shown at the 1949 Olympics at Wembley. Because the sound of the starter's pistol takes a little longer to reach the man on the outside than on the inside lane the starting pistol was so arranged that every runner was exactly the same distance from the operator. We had electrical methods of judging "hits" in the fencing and special devices for judging the broad jump. We are no longer content with the old idea which still rules in baseball that "the umpire's decision is final." The question of whether one man has run faster than another has become so important that we demand it be decided by methods as precise as those used in engineering.

There will obviously be further developments in this direction. Once it is admitted that it is important to avoid an error in placing men an inch apart at the end of a race, it is essential to decide whether they started at the same moment. The present method of starting is nearly as crude as the old method of timing. We may see "starting blocks" in which the runner's heels are electrically locked until the starting gun is fired so that any possibility of "beating the gun" is avoided. Already there are miniature attachments for players and runners who can thus receive instructions while an event is in progress.

The camera, now extensively used for deciding the winner of a race, will be brought into use for giving decisions in other sports where it is considered that the human eye is too easily deceived. It is now possible to produce a photograph that can be examined within a matter of seconds from the finish of a race, and the future rules for football or boxing may demand that a continuous photographic record is made of the contest so that any decision which is challenged can be decided by the camera. In fact, it would be simpler in boxing to have an electrical machine which would register those blows struck below the belt which cause so many disputes. There would be no difficulty in producing such a device and it would not encumber the boxers. A German, before the war, invented a "robot" boxer which dodged and weaved like a human being and registered electrically the number, position and force of the blows it was struck. At the end of a bout these could be computed and a far more accurate estimate of a boxer's ability obtained than by merely watching for "points."

Professional boxing is a coarse and sometimes a dangerous sport against which educated people, who show an increasing distaste of physical display, will probably revolt. It will be quite simple for scientists to save the sport from extinction, make it very much more dependent upon skill and remove the need for physical damage. The boxers will have to wear special light clothing in which electrical contacts will be concealed. Every blow received will be registered and will be flashed to a board so that the spectators can follow the progress of the fight. Thus boxing would follow the development of fencing which from an art concerned with running an opponent through in battle or a duel has become a blameless sport in which recording methods are becoming quite popular. There is, of course, still the important argument that, if contestants could not be hurt, attendances might be so reduced that the financial benefits would be seriously affected.

Radar type apparatus may one day come to be used for controlling ball games. It would not be difficult to provide an invisible "net" that would decide whether a ball in baseball was good or not and possibly l.b.w. disputes in cricket could be eliminated in the same way. Metal stumps and bails and an electrical "contact" line in place of the batting crease would save all argument as to "run out" decisions, the exact relative moments of the removal of the bails and the foot crossing the crease could be recorded. There is no sport to which science could not make further contributions in the interests of fair play. Automatic batsmen are also quite within the scope of possible design. Automatic bowlers and machines for "firing" golf balls have long been in service together with the most complicated ballistic apparatus for the testing of various ball flights under a wide mixture of mathematical theories.

To many it may seem absurd that so much effort and ingenuity should be spent to eliminate or reduce the possibility of human error in the result of a "sporting" contest. Sportsmen of all kinds assure you that it is the game that matters and not the result. But, for good or ill, during the last fifty years these events have come to have extraordinary importance for millions of people. The headlines "Disasters for England" do not suggest the unbalancing of the budget, defeat of armies or the death of leading statesmen; only that her first four or five batsmen playing against Australia have allowed themselves to be deceived by a cricket ball rather earlier than anticipated. To what lengths the glorification of professional sport will be carried is difficult to forecast, but it is certain that there is no immediate sign of the reversal of this trend. On the contrary, rapid transport makes it possible to consider "world championships." Not so long ago local villages played against each other in games and were content. Now "leagues" extend all over the country and "players" think nothing of travelling hundreds of miles in a day to take part in games. Formerly "internationals" between distant countries were rarities. Now they occur in some form nearly every week. The tendency is towards a world "league" and when Australia is brought within a few hours' flying time of Britain, "tests" will be played every year in each country, instead of every five years. The limit to the development of spectacular sport seems to be purely commercial and we must now regard sport in the same light as any other form of mass entertainment.

Only comparatively wealthy countries can afford to make sport a national industry or, indeed, indulge in it at all. The mass attraction of sport to-day is abnormal rather than normal. We have to go back to the Roman Empire to find anything which it resembles. Whether this is progress or not is a matter of opinion, but the reasons generally put forward in support of sport hardly bear examination. It is suggested, as far as international sport is concerned, that it is excellent in promoting understanding and brotherhood. Here the facts hardly support the argument. International sporting contests have only too often been marred by acrimonious arguments and have left a feeling, not of brotherhood, but of bitterness. The "body line" controversy in cricket came near to endangering the friendship of Australia and England, a fantastic state of affairs when we consider that not an inch of land, not a penny and not even an idea was at stake. The visit of the Moscow Dynamo footballers to Britain did nothing to improve relations between the countries. On the contrary, the meeting of eleven men from each of the two countries to kick a rubber and leather ball was interpreted politically so as to accentuate differences. The Germans used the Olympic Games to publicise their way of life and government, as if the fact that one man could run or jump better than another could "prove" anything politically, philosophically or socially.

It is also suggested that sport is an excellent thing because it keeps people healthy and "fit." This rules out the millions who take no part in sport except as spectators and raises the question of for what purpose it keeps its participants fit. The answer is that it keeps them fit for the sport, and nothing else. We hear of boxers who work as blacksmiths to make them fitter for the ring, but I have yet to hear of the blacksmith who takes up boxing to make himself fit for the smithy. There does not seem to be any scientific evidence that people who indulge in strenuous sports are any "fitter" than people who do not, that they become ill less often or that they live longer.

Another argument in favour of sport is that it encourages a sense of fair play and develops that elusive thing called "character." There may be some truth in this statement, although if it were a genuine reason for sport, one would expect chess and billiards to be encouraged as much as football and boxing, since such tournaments call for no less fair play and avoid the risk of danger to life and limb, as well as taking considerably less space. The public would not pay to watch these games very readily. In fact, the origin of all sport in the usual sense lay in the need for food or in training for war.

A view rarely advanced is that sport is good because it gives pleasure. It is undoubtedly the reason why the majority of people indulge in sports; they enjoy them. But this reason is rarely heard, perhaps because it might lead to an enquiry as to whether the pleasure is of a desirable kind. Nearly all people take pleasure in many things which are illegal or undesirable and the mere fact that a pursuit gives satisfaction cannot be considered alone to be sufficient justification.

This consideration of the basis for mass indulgence in sport is put forward because in the future the trend may be reversed. We may come to consider that the devotion of a large part of the national income, which means the work of a great number of people, to sport, is not allowable. The cult of sport has been established in the last century largely as a result of mass propaganda and it would not be hard to reverse the process so that spending an entire day trying to knock a small ball into a hole in the ground was considered unfashionable or even a sign of mental deficiency. There will be no sudden and dramatic revolt against sport, but rather a steady substitution of scientific sports for those which we have adapted from the simple balls and clubs that were all our ancestors had available.

In the last few decades there has been an enormous increase of public interest in motor racing of various kinds, a sport which is "useful" in a way that cricket and football could never be. Many of the major improvements in cars and motorcycles, such as supercharging, overhead valves and improved fuels, have come as a result of racing and record breaking. The success of a dirt-track rider depends to some extent on his skill in preparing his machine as well as his skill in handling it. In the near future we may expect developments of great interest by such things as the use of rockets to gain rapid acceleration in all kinds of motor racing. "Speeding up" is only another phrase for civilisation and we are observing its effects even in the more conservative sports, such as fishing where "radar" has been used to detect fish. Deep-sea fishing has been conducted with radio attachments to a harpooned fish and there seems no reason why such an apparatus should not be attached to a fox.

It is, perhaps, a pity that the tradition of "working sport" has almost died out. Covent Garden porters used to test their skill in carrying baskets; Paris waiters, their speed and sense of balance in racing with loaded trays. Tree-felling has become an established sport in Australia and log-rolling in Canada. But there are great possibilities for the development of more mechanised sports in connection with industry. We may yet see competitions between giant grabs removing a pile of debris, it is plain from the crowds of "rubber necks" who watch "men at work" that this kind of thing has a certain spectacular appeal and it has the advantage over older sports in that it is useful. As in motor racing, manufacturers would be stimulated to produce faster, more reliable and more efficient machines.

Or we may see races between radio-controlled planes in which there will be a test not only of mechanism but of the skill of the controllers. The development of such sports seems to be foreshadowed by the extreme interest of the younger generation in such things as powered aircraft models. Young men would take more readily to the sport of kings if the new electronic jockey became fashionable. Human beings are less and less inclined to physical effort and it has been said that one day a dancer will expect to stand still while the floor does the work. All motion, we shall be told, is relative.

It is very much more useful and sensible to engage in sports which stimulate quality and research that can be applied in industry. Science has contributed a great deal to all sports. Tennis balls are now kept in refrigerators so that they will have a uniform bounce. Footballs are tested for their bounce by ingenious machines instead of by the naked eye. New methods of making golf balls have been devised which make them travel farther and truer. Even fishing reels have been improved so that errors on the part of the angler do not result in over-running or breakage. In the not distant future we may see the same urge applied to sports derived from more productive industry. There are many precedents. The bullfight and, more recently, the rodeo, evolved from purely utilitarian practices into pure "sports." Early aviation was greatly stimulated by the sporting element, the development of the aircraft for military and commercial purposes came much later. Without the early races and meetings the aeroplane might have remained for many years as a clumsy and useless affair of "bamboo and string."

The desire for competition in some form seems fundamental in the majority of human beings. It would be fantastic to suppose that it will rapidly disappear. We may only hope that the curious idea of national glory attached to success in sports will disappear as rapidly as it appeared and that our grandchildren will be puzzled to understand why we considered that a man who ran a mile in four minutes or knocked a ball into a hole with fewer strokes, somehow or other brought credit to the country in which he was born or lived, it is not always clear which applies. But the instinct of rivalry and competition will remain and may well change the forms in which it finds expression. Many of our present sports will seem to future generations as quaint, childish or brutal as tilting the quintain and bear-baiting are to us to-day.

There seems little doubt that the popularity of so-called "blood sports" is waning and that they will disappear in the near future. These sports were derived from the days when hunting was necessary for food or for the control of harmful or dangerous animals. When hunting was necessary, the hunters could not afford to be "sporting." The element of sport increased as the necessity for the pursuit and killing disappeared. Hunts of different kind became hedged with as many conventions as was specialised duelling in its dying days. It was "sport" to catch trout with a certain type of equipment, but not with another or by "tickling," which actually might call for far more skill. It is sport to pursue a fox with a certain type of dog, wearing a certain uniform, but not to shoot it, which is often more difficult. Bullfighting has become associated with such a ritual that the actual "fighting" is now a minor part of the display.

A study of history suggests that this process of conventionalising sport will continue until it becomes more and more remote from reality. Eventually, perhaps, we shall have hunters still wearing the same uniform, travelling across country on horses or even in shooting brakes, in pursuit of a non-existent fox. They will be quite as satisfied with the competition and display as we are to-day with any number of old customs, the purpose of which has completely disappeared but which are still faithfully observed in form, if not in spirit.

We may deplore the pursuit and killing of animals for pleasure not only for the sake of the animals which may suffer but because we believe the pleasure experienced, however genuine, is bad. But it will be better to "educate" away blood sports rather than to legislate them out of existence. The instincts to which they appeal might take other channels, and while it is impossible to judge between two wrongs, it is better that a few people should chase foxes until they are weaned to some sensible pursuit than that they should engage in man-hunts or lynchings which are the form our hunting memories take in some parts of the world. Blood sports will die a natural death in Britain and other civilised countries in due course.

Any consideration of the use to which men and women will put their very considerable leisure in the future must involve such philosophical questions as the purpose of life. At the moment the vast majority of people have given this matter little thought. There are growing signs that a certain number are not content to "do nothing" or to pursue pleasure and that even more are vaguely aware of a distrust of time that brings no satisfaction. These are a very small proportion, for those in authority have been content to win leisure for the people without giving any opportunity for its advantageous use. The final triumph of mechanised industry has always been a reduction in working hours, seldom greater satisfaction for its members in their leisure. Few organisations are expressly concerned with what their members do in the time won on their behalf. The idea of a beautiful and joyous use of a non-working period seems to be bounded by the principle of regimented amusement.

We have had a large leisured class for such a short time that the deeper implications have hardly arisen. In the past this numerically small body has been responsible for much of our artistic, scientific and academic progress. We are approaching the time when the majority of human beings will belong to the "idle classes." It will present many problems, some of which have been indicated, but it will be a tragedy indeed if science having provided the leisure, men and women can find no better use for it than in the days when every spare moment was something snatched from strenuous labour and devoted to a search for forgetfulness.

CHAPTER 5

RADIO IN THE FUTURE

THE most popular form of entertainment to-day in most industrialised countries is undoubtedly "listening to the wireless." Millions spend as many hours a week listening as at work; even then the aether provides music. For most people, indeed, "wireless" means no more than the distribution of amusement or information. Undoubtedly, broadcasting will continue to occupy much of our so-called spare time in the future and we can expect to see certain technical advances, apart from the distant possibilities of broadcasting scent and touch as well as sound and sight.

The most important alteration in the near future **is**

likely to be a change from amplitude to frequency modulation, a technical step which may bring a number of advantages. As the names imply, the difference between the two systems is that, in one, signals are given by modulation of the amplitude of the waves, and in the other, by modulation of frequency. We need not concern ourselves with technicalities. Frequency modulation was one original method used in wireless transmission, but it was abandoned in favour of A.M. until quite lately when Armstrong, inventor of the "super-het" which so greatly improved the quality of wireless receivers, returned to the study of F.M. and produced it in a practical form.

The advantages of F.M. are greater faithfulness in reproduction and greater selectivity. All reproduced music or speech is, in a sense, an illusion. The thought that someone is inside a radio set or that a violin is playing, is as much of an illusion as the ventriloquist's dummy. The sounds that issue forth are not the same as we should hear if we were in the studio with the speaker or the violinist. They only approximate to reality. Our ears, however, readily lend themselves to deception. Given the reproduction of certain frequencies, we "imagine" the others, or at least we do not find that their absence entirely ruins the music. The degree to which we enjoy illusion varies not only with the individual, but with habit. A listener with a "poor" wireless set does not notice the distortion whereas a sensitive stranger, hearing it for the first time, finds it horrible. It is very easy by constantly listening to a badly distorting set, and all sets distort to a certain degree, to believe that the sounds are very natural. It is only when we hear far better reproduction that we realise how vastly different is most reception to the "real" sounds.

The best F.M. receivers are able to give a faithfulness of reproduction that is a revelation to listeners accustomed even to good A.M. reproduction. For this reason alone all broadcasting is likely in due course to change to F.M.

Unfortunately a receiver designed for A.M. is not easily adapted to F.M. and the change therefore must be made slowly over the course of a number of years to avoid millions of listeners finding themselves suddenly faced with the alternative of buying a new set or being deprived of entertainment.

The other advantage of F.M. is still more important. Because this type of transmission requires so narrow a wave band that stations can operate close together on almost identical frequencies without interference, the F.M. system makes it possible to double, treble and even quadruple the number of transmitters in a country without interference with each other. In the United States, where greater progress has been made with F.M. than elsewhere, hundreds of transmitters may be added to those already in existence. The estimated total number of stations possible is about 3,000, and the importance of this change lies in the fact that the limited number of transmitters which it has been possible to operate in any area has always been the excuse to make broadcasting a monopoly. With the coming of F.M. the erection of transmitters will have to continue to be closely controlled, but it will be a simple matter to open them to many different interests. Moreover, the cost of an F.M. transmitter is much lower than that of existing plant and it is feasible for such bodies as municipalities, learned societies and universities to have their own transmitters.

Doubtless the monopolists will fight to retain their privilege, but radio could be very much more "regional." Many programmes which would be of interest in a comparatively small locality, such as the transmission of debates on local government, have never been considered because the requirements of listeners over a very much larger area have had to be met. With fifty or a hundred transmitters instead of half a dozen, it will be practicable to offer a better choice without finding it so necessary to consider the lowest common denominator in the tastes of millions of listeners. F.M. may make it possible to devote one or two stations purely to the transmission of data. We might, for example, have a radio "clock," a transmitter that did nothing but send out the time. Radio engineers would no doubt be interested in a transmitter sending out a standard frequency for checking. But the chief importance of F.M. should be its opportunity to restore freedom to the air.

Other important developments of the near future in radio communication are its adaptation to railways and motor-cars. High frequency radio on railways should enable us to improve many types of signalling which are still extremely crude. It needs only a fog to reduce railways to chaos. Direct radio communication between driver, signal cabin and the drivers of other trains should make it much easier to speed up traffic. The present difficulty faced by all railways is that safety must be the first consideration and radio signalling cannot be introduced until there is perfect confidence that the method will be mistake- and fool-proof. The use of radio signalling for speeding up work in marshalling yards has already been demonstrated, the great advantage being that radio, unlike visual communication, is not interrupted by weather. It is ridiculous that an aircraft travelling at high speed can be "talked down" by radio in fog, whereas a 5 m.p.h. goods train is brought to a standstill.

The installation of miniature transmitters in cars and even in small suitcases is limited by the available wavelengths, but improved transmitters will become commonly used by people to whom instant communication is important—the Press, the Police, doctors and business men. In the not distant future every policeman will probably be equipped with a short range transmitter of very light weight, enabling him to get into instant touch with his headquarters. Radio will also be increasingly applied to

safety devices. The householder of the future will be able
to carry a small gadget in his pocket that will emit an
audible signal if a burglar forces his way into his house
or if a fire breaks out. It would be simple to devise an
instrument that would "ring" the householder wherever
he was, if the telephone in his home or office was calling.
It could be arranged that he would only need to go to the
nearest telephone to have the call put through to him on
the spot.

Ever since the invention of radio transmission men have
dreamed of being able to transmit energy, and we have had
pictures of the future in which light and heat were transmitted through the aether from central generating stations.
Unfortunately, although a radio signal may be highly
directional, the proportion of the energy received is ex-
ceedingly small compared with that transmitted. Even
with the pulse transmission used in radar, in which the
energy is saved up to be transmitted in bursts, the quantity
received at a distance of a few miles is not sufficient to
disturb a fly, much less light a lamp. Enough energy to
light a lamp can be transmitted to a distance of a few
yards, and no doubt this distance will be increased, but the
method is absurdly inefficient as compared with transmission through solid conductors. Far too much energy is
dissipated. It is still not fully realised by many that the
"energy" used in a radio receiver for producing the sound
in the loudspeaker is supplied from the receiver's battery
or mains and not from the transmission, which merely
varies the locally available energy.

Except for special purposes where efficiency is unimportant compared with the mere fact of transmission the
radio transmission of power for heating and lighting cannot be expected in the near future. This, for many years,
rules out the radio propelled motor-car or aeroplane. It is
possible, however, that if electrical power became far
cheaper it might be used for propelling land vehicles by

induction. The power would be transmitted to a buried conductor under all leading roads, and would be picked up by any vehicle travelling above its area. The "engine" would be little more than a simple electric motor and there would be great advantages in smooth running, absence of noise, no fumes and no fuel troubles. The question of charging for electrical energy would be quickly solved by the installation of a meter to register the energy consumed. Small scale installations of this kind have already been used for trolleys in one or two factories in the U.S.S.R. Local lighting and heating may follow.

Although we can rule out radio-powered aircraft and cars, radio-controlled transport is another matter. In radio control the energy required to propel the vehicle, aircraft or ship, is produced locally as well as the energy required to operate the controls. The radio transmission decides which controls are operated as in the case of the military use of radio controls. The non-military possibilities include the operation of railways without drivers and guards —the G.P.O. already run a small underground railway for the conveyance of mail in this fashion—and the control from a single ship of convoys of freighters without crews. The disadvantage of radio control, that it can only be effective when the controlled ship is within view, can be overcome by the installation of automatic transmitters which send back information and give the exact position of the controlled unit. Beam control can also be applied.

The deciding factor is the cost of installation and except, possibly, in the case of passenger or cargo ferries working over short distances, it seems unlikely that the radio control of ships will be of much importance for commercial purposes. For piloting, or part automatic control systems and for ships in narrow waters radio control will extend rapidly. Fog causes enormous losses at some ports and in the comparatively near future we may expect all ships to be equipped with anti-collision radar devices and receivers which will enable them to operate in poor visibility.

It is probable that, in the air, radio control will be used for operating freight and mail planes. These aircraft will operate on radio beams, being taken under control by an operator on the ground when they are signalled as nearing the airport.

One of the great developments in radio communication is likely to be the perfection of rapid and efficient methods for transmitting the printed or written word. The radio transmission of pictures has been common for twenty years and has been used not only for Press photographs, but for cheques and fingerprints. The quality of the facsimile has improved tremendously, but the method remains relatively slow, and although it would be possible to transmit a page of a newspaper in this way the advantages over transmission of the actual words, as distinct from the "picture" they make, is not great.

Some ten years ago satisfactory progress had been made in radio pictures and letter facsimile designed especially for the transmission of newspapers. The object was to provide a means by which a journal could be produced in a small installation in any house instead of being printed at a central office and distributed by train, truck or hand. Technical difficulties were considerable other than for visual observation. When a permanent record was needed most systems called for sensitized paper and processing which seriously increased the cost of operation. Under various new systems many of these troubles have been overcome, experimental newspapers have been transmitted and it is likely that within at most a few decades we shall be able to come down to breakfast and find a small stop-press newspaper "fresh off the press" in the radio set. Instead of being five to twelve hours old, the printed news will be up-to-the-minute, with perhaps a few new pages to be printed while the first sheet is being read.

Technical progress may well outstrip commercial production because the radio newspaper involves certain economic problems. Who is to pay for the paper? Perhaps it will be the advertiser who will pay so that the paper can be distributed free. Who is to pay for the installation? Will the ordinary man consider the advantages sufficient to justify paying £50 for a radio newspaper receiver instead of one penny a day? All these points are economic rather than scientific, although the radio engineer may help to solve some of these seeming drawbacks. He could, for instance, provide a device which, unless it were installed in the receiver, would make it impossible to receive the "scrambled" transmission and this apparatus could be rented to the subscriber by the proprietors of the journal.

Such an idea, popularly called "pay or squeal" because unless it is installed the radio receiver squeals instead of giving intelligible signals, may be used to solve the difficulty of making economic radio transmissions of various kinds without the disadvantages of state monopoly or advertising sponsorship.

"Facsimile," obviously, has possibilities quite apart from the production of newspapers. Business would benefit by a method of almost instantly transmitting documents to any part of the world and a really efficient method of sending whole pages of manuscript or print over long distances would eliminate the need for some air mail. A development of the outfit already in use by the Radio Corporation of America, known as Ultrafax, is likely to prove revolutionary in the field of communications. It is past the experimental stage but not yet in "mass production" and it is difficult to resist the idea that within the next ten years it may make some of our present methods of communication, from air mail to long distance telegraphy, entirely obsolete.

The principle on which Ultrafax works is simple. The picture, printed page or manuscript, to be transmitted, is placed before a television camera. This takes a "still" which is transmitted as signals in exactly the same way as a television picture, but at the receiving end, instead of being flashed on to a screen it is brought before a high speed camera which photographs it, develops, prints and dries the print in a few seconds. The total time required for the whole operation from beginning to end is less than one minute, most of which is taken up by processing at the receiver. At the end of this minute an exact reproduction of the picture or page is ready many miles away. The invention is no more than the wedding of television to photography and its great advantage over any other means of communication, including radio-telephony, is speed. A transmitter can deal with up to 1,000 pictures or pages of a printed book in one minute. The receiver requires longer for processing, but by installing a number of receiving cameras, it would be possible for the reception to take place equally fast. As a demonstration, the whole of that exceptionally long novel *Gone With the Wind,* consisting of 1,037 pages and one million words, was transmitted in less than ninety seconds. No other means approaches this for speed and there is the further advantage over radio-telephony that the words are permanently recorded. The fastest methods of telegraphy do not compete.

At the present time this new system suffers from the same disadvantage as television in that its unaided range is limited. The direct range is theoretically set by the optical horizon for transmission through the aether. In practice, this means fifty to one hundred miles according to conditions, but there are several methods of overcoming this difficulty, such as the use of bouncer stations as in television. With the possible exception of confidential documents picture telegraphy is likely to supersede the older telegraph and its hand or automatic sending. In the future, the telegram, exactly as written, will be clipped to a travelling band, carried before a television camera and within one minute a facsimile of the telegram will be available in the receiving office, ready for delivery. Apart from saving time, there is immense saving of labour. Because of its simplicity, speed and, when fully developed, cheapness, this system may replace a certain amount of air mail. It will not pay to transport letters for delivery a day or two later when it is as cheap to transmit them in a few seconds.

The question of secrecy will no doubt arise, but will hardly cause much trouble other than in special cases. It is theoretically true that the transmission could be "tapped" for the purpose of reading other people's letters, but this would call for an elaborate installation and could mostly be circumvented by "scrambling" the signals during transmission so that only a meaningless jumble would be picked up by any receiver not "coded" to the transmitter. The great speed of operation may mean that, in time, it will be simpler to send a facsimile of this kind than to post a letter in any big town. For sixpence or a shilling, we shall be able to hand in a letter at the post office and have it delivered at a distant town within an hour.

The system has been taken up by Western Union in the United States who state that in due course much of their $1\frac{3}{4}$ million miles of telegraph wire may come down. It must be some years before it is economic to install this type of facsimile receiver in every village, but for large centres of population it seems destined to replace the telegraph before very long. Apparatus in this field is no more than the adaption of television to the transmission of "still" pictures. Instead of transmitting some twenty-five slightly different pictures of a moving scene every second, to give the illusion of movement, the transmitter deals with a number of separate pictures, the number being limited by the mechanical process of passing the pages in front of the camera rather than by the speed of camera and transmitter.

It is limitation in range that is one of the serious problems of all television in the future. There are at the moment several different methods by which shortness of range can be overcome and it is uncertain which will prove the most successful. There seems little hope, with our present knowledge, of increasing reception distance by any new method of televising, for short range is an inherent property of the very high frequencies required for television. Good reception is limited to the optical horizon, the higher the transmitting aerial the greater the range, and by carrying the aerial on a fixed balloon or a circling aircraft it is possible to increase the range to hundreds of miles, the exact distance depending upon the height of the aircraft. Television signals would have to be transmitted by a directional transmitter to the aircraft from which they would be relayed to every part of the country visible from its height. Using such a system, four or five planes would enable the whole of the British Isles to be covered.

This system has been tried experimentally and there do not appear to be any technical difficulties which could not be overcome. The method has certain disadvantages, the aircraft requires a considerable power supply and must carry a bulky transmitter. Cost is high, but not unduly so when other methods of increasing range are considered. It is possible that in the future freight and mail planes flying regular routes and time-tables all over the world might be harnessed to relay television signals. The planes would not only pass signals down to receivers at ground level but also relay them to each other, thus eventually bridging thousands of miles.

Another more immediately practical method of increasing range is by the use of relay stations within "sight" of each other. The main transmitter radiates signals which not only serve receivers within, say, fifty miles, but are also picked up by a relaying station which in turn passes them on to another relaying station until they reach the second main transmitter which "broadcasts" them at full power. The disadvantage is a slight reduction in faithfulness of reproduction which is almost inevitable at each relay.

The system now generally used for medium range increase is the co-axial cable. This is a special type of multi-cable which can carry the high frequency signals required for television. It is very expensive compared with the line used for the transmission of ordinary telephone signals, but some thousands of miles of it are being laid down in the United States to link up the large cities; within the next ten years it seems certain that several hundred of the towns in all parts of the North American continent will be joined in this way. A combination of relays and co-axial cables is likely to be used during the next stage of television's development, but where an ocean link is necessary such as New York to London there appears to be no immediate solution. The transatlantic telegraph cable must have appeared equally difficult to pioneers of the telegraph and we may expect that improvements in directional transmission will solve the problem long before aircraft relays or even the construction of an artificial satellite become essential. Transatlantic vision is a necessity of the near future.

Television is, at present, not much more than a novel form of entertainment, although few who have had experience of it can doubt that it will soon completely replace "sound-only" broadcasting. The appeal to the additional sense is irresistible and adds great realism. It may be felt that sight adds little to the reading of a news bulletin, for we have become so accustomed to listening "blind" that we now hardly miss the appeal to the eye. But a new generation will take seeing for granted and in due course all telephones will have a screen for showing the speaker. We talk not only with the words we utter but also with our faces, even with our hands, and there are many telephone misunderstandings which would never have occurred if it had been possible for eyes to see the truth.

Television as an entertainment will develop as fast as capital expenditure allows. Mass production should make it possible to produce receivers for less than half the present price and within twenty years a television receiver in every home will be considered as necessary as is a sound set at this moment. Screens will be far larger with full cinema dimensions for public simultaneous viewing of current events. By this time we may have heard our last "sound-only" entertainment, although it might be produced from time to time as a nostalgic novelty just as "silent" films are occasionally shown to-day. The "advance" in realism of television over sound-only transmission is greater than that of the talking picture compared with the silent screen because the sense of sight is often far more important than that of hearing. In the silent days the sense of hearing was, to a limited extent, covered by music to prevent the "sound" of silence.

Our next stage will be coloured television, already perfected experimentally. Its commercial appearance, however, is likely to be considerably delayed, for it implies the construction of new cameras and transmitting equipment as well as new receivers. The film in colour did not call for the replacement of projection equipment, the same projector can show either monochrome or coloured films. At present it does not seem possible to design a television receiver which could equally well receive grey or multi-coloured transmissions. But without such an invention the transition stage from black and white to colour may have to be long postponed because of the difficulties that would arise. As for stereoscopy, this would appear to be impossible in the mathematical sense unless the viewers wear glasses but there are several methods of imitating the desired result to some extent. For the home receiver it is by no means an insoluble problem.

Television, now mainly an amusement, will prove to have many more important uses. The installation of television cameras in operating theatres is already helping surgeons to demonstrate with greater comfort and safety. Students sit in a separate room and can see much more clearly the surgeon talking to them with a throat or chest microphone. Television will be important in all branches of education and for certain technical subjects has already been exploited by the U.S. Navy. The television screen may largely replace the blackboard in schools. It could revolutionise present methods, the "live" teacher acting as a tutor while the demonstration is made by carefully chosen specialists on the screen. Although teaching is sometimes the last refuge of those who can pass examinations but do little more, in fact, it requires quite exceptional gifts. The gifted teacher is almost as rare and certainly as talented as the greatest actress or musician, but because it is necessary to find a few hundred thousand teachers for our children, we refuse to recognise the facts and put up with an archaic system. Sound broadcasting and the film have been useful in thousands of schools, but television is still more valuable and offers immense possibilities by its instantaneous appeal to the eye and ear.

Television will also be important in crime detection. The communication of descriptions, photographs and fingerprints will be quicker and more simple. In the future we might well have identity parades in which the suspect is intermingled with people hundreds of miles away. Television "watch-dogs" will enable the police to look into banks and other important places at night without opening doors. By using infra-red instead of white-light-sensitive cameras the burglar might be televised at work and watched from the nearest police station without his being aware of it at any time. World "hook ups" by television will enable statesmen and others to meet in conference without having to spend time and trouble in travelling thousands of miles. "Mixing" their images would enable them to talk things over round a conference table almost as effectively as if they were actually together.

The question of television as a competitor with other forms of entertainment can well be left to time, for it is obvious that it has come to stay and that it will compete, not altogether in the harmful manner so often visualised by sports promoters, theatre owners or cinema managers. The history of the cinema and sound broadcasting during the last thirty years should have taught that it is of little use to halt progress by "boycott." Each in turn has been proclaimed as heralding the end of theatre or "live" concert but each in turn has proved to have done nothing of the kind and to-day there are larger theatre or concert audiences than ever.

Reality has always its own value. The reproduction of a boxing match, even with full sound and colour, still falls far short of the facts when the sounds reproduced are not selected. Atmosphere cannot be reproduced. Television is an intimate art and should we, in time, succeed in reproducing the sense of touch and of smell it is inconceivable that the degree of accuracy for many centuries would be sufficient to compare with living entertainment. Television may influence the form of our theatre as in the case of films and radio, but beyond that it can do little more until the day when all physical movement is regarded as atavistic.

CHAPTER 6

HEALTH AND MEDICINE IN THE FUTURE

ENJOYMENT of work, and indeed of all living, depends upon good health. In other ages life was usually short and often brutish. Sickness and death were looked upon as sent by the "Gods" so that very little interference seemed possible. Good health was regarded solely as a much-to-be-desired gift.

The advance in science and medicine during the last two centuries has shown that while health may be very much a matter of fortune we are now inclined to attribute it to our parents. We also know there is much that can be done to ensure it by human intervention. It is natural, therefore, that health should become a major pre-occupation of civilised man.

About one-twentieth of the national income of Britain is now spent on health.* It is more than is spent on education or even upon entertainment and about half that spent on the armed forces. It is doubtful whether any country at any other period has spent so lavishly on its health. The immediate result is hospitals filled to overflowing, queues at doctors' surgeries, dentists finding it impossible to see all their would-be patients and the average person suffering statistically from seventeen major and minor illnesses a year. Statistically, Britain and other leading industrial nations are healthier than they have ever been. The death-rate is lower, the chance of survival to old age much greater and the promise of relief from one of a hundred different diseases almost certain. But there remains the fact that health and illness have almost become obsessions and that the treatment of ill-health is now a major industry. The paradox will not escape future historians.

During the next few decades there will be many notable advances in medicine and we may expect to see new diseases discovered and others added to the already long list of ills from which a cure can be "guaranteed" or immunity secured. But it will be surprising if, on the whole, the illness ratio is reduced during the next ten or twenty years. There is, as it were, a vested interest in ill-health, both in the medical profession and in our social system. Doctors do not desire illness in their patients and people do not want to be ill, but our concern is almost wholly with the sick, who are abnormal and not with the healthy. It is an interesting speculation as to what would happen if instead of paying compensation to a sick person, the state paid a bonus to every individual for every week he

* In the United States less than one-fiftieth of the national income was spent on health and medical services in 1949.

remained well. Insurance companies long ago recognised this principle and the "no claim bonus" probably has a salutary effect on reducing the number of minor accidents.

In the instance of wild animals and in many primitive tribes the sick, far from receiving sympathy, are treated with the gravest suspicion and sometimes they are killed. Sympathy with the sick is, in terms of human history, partly a new idea; a gigantic health service, absorbing an appreciable part of the national effort, is its logical development. The feelings involved are so obviously right by civilised standards that no one has questioned the desirability of providing for every person the best possible treatment, regardless of cost. No one, however, has paused to consider what is happening. If we plot graphs representing the cost per patient, the number of hospital beds per 1,000 people, the number of doctors, nurses or any other expenditure on health services, against the passing of the years, we find that the line in each case is accelerating rapidly towards infinity. The number of doctors has doubled in a comparatively short period, the expenditure per patient has trebled and the number of laboratory tests has been more than quadrupled. None of the increases shows signs of evening to steadiness. We are told we need a minimum of another 15,000 doctors. Every year new laboratory tests are invented which undoubtedly improve the chances of accurate diagnosis.

All these indications show that producing the curve of the graph is justified and that by about A.D. 2000 half the nation will be engaged in providing medical services for the other half. This is, of course, absurd for it is obvious that the whole economy of the nation would break down. Yet no one has yet considered the point at which we shall say, "Stop, even if some people suffer or die we cannot provide more medicine." We know now that there are diseases, such as tuberculosis, which are largely diseases of poverty; the incidence is very low with well-to-do people.

No doubt we shall discover other diseases which can be avoided by having more money. Health, in a degree, will always be purchasable, for the man with unlimited money can live in a way which reduces the chances of his suffering a whole series of organic and mental troubles. In spite of a "free" health service, medicine is still a matter of money. In an ideal world everyone would have enough money to avoid occupational or sociological disease and this, logically, is the ideal at which social medicine is aiming. Yet no one who examines the problem soberly believes such a solution to be possible, as will be seen when this subject is considered more fully; the point is that in the future there will be many medical discoveries which cannot conceivably help everyone without restriction.

Let us look at some of the discoveries that are certain in the comparatively near future. Extensive research upon substances derived from moulds suggests that during the next few years a number will be found to attack disease-causing organisms which are immune from attack by penicillin, the first of the moulds to be used in this way. One of the new types is streptomycin and it is being increasingly used. All of them, no doubt, will have certain disadvantages, but within thirty years we may expect to have materials which will destroy the organisms responsible for whooping cough, infantile paralysis and many other infectious diseases at present beyond our control. This advance will save millions of lives but may well be accompanied by the appearance of new diseases or of old diseases in new forms. Already medicine has discovered "penicillin-resisting" strains of organisms of the type which ought to be destroyed but which, in fact, are immune. The theory is that these strains have always existed in comparatively small numbers, together with organisms that are destroyed by penicillin. When the latter are killed, the first strain is left with a "free field" and begins to multiply. The problem is likely to be extremely difficult for medicine, because it suggests that the "curing" of a disease is not nearly as simple as it has appeared.

It is hard, if not impossible with our limited knowledge, to foresee the result of interfering with the processes of an "organism" as complicated as the body. We have an analogy in the technique of deliberately breeding one animal or insect to attack others considered harmful. The mongoose was introduced into the West Indies to rid them of a plague of rats. The mongoose destroyed the rats but then turned its attention to poultry, doing as much damage as the original rats. There have been similar examples when insects have been introduced as parasites upon some other harmful class. The parasite destroyed the harmful insect, but itself became a danger. In the same way we have discovered that by adding certain chemicals and minerals to the soil we can increase the yield of crops and are only now learning that this is not the whole story. The crops are increased immediately, but the full effect of the chemicals is not always apparent for ten or twenty years when it might be found that they have so altered the nature of the soil as to render it no longer safely fertile or incapable of resisting other types of parasitic attack.

Perhaps we shall observe the same effect in the case of the human body. Doctors can provide treatment for almost every condition. The symptoms and the condition may disappear and that, as far as the doctor is concerned, is the end of the matter. But is it always the end? Is it not possible that the treatment for one disease has made the patient more susceptible to a host of others? Shall we discover that the real cause of the endless coughs, colds, rheumatics and other minor aches and pains which now seem to afflict the public lies in the very "cures" we have discovered for other ailments? That is one leading argument of the "Nature" healers, and orthodox medicine may in the not distant future give some attention to such a point of view and react against the specialisation which has become greater in recent years. The organs of our body have been so far separated on paper that one man treats the heart, another the liver and yet another the brain. Human beings function as a whole and one mild danger of specialisation is that the specialist tends to look at all symptoms in terms of his own pre-conceived opinion.

Medicine has its fashions no less than dress. We have seen the removal of the appendix or of the tonsils regarded almost as "cure-alls." Then with the discovery of vitamins came the tendency to regard them as the secret of all good health. We had only to take the right vitamins and we should be well. In due course new discoveries were made, more vitamins, more about minute quantities of different minerals which play an important part in health, and these became the fashionable explanation of every trouble. Those minute organisms, the viruses, were found and anything that could not be otherwise explained was put down to the virus. In the future we shall make discoveries, each of which will be "epoch-making" and will, until the next discovery, be regarded as the explanation of all unexplained illness. The Bacteriophage is already striving for popularity and although the advances made by medical science cannot be belittled during a demand for the "best" medical treatment for everyone, we must be warned against the mechanisation of medicine upon the factory line method accompanied by a series of pre-natal, natal and adolescent injections at every local clinic.

The tendency will be for the patient to pass before a series of doctors, rather as in an army examination, each of whom will examine him for some detail and then pass him on to the next booth. At the end of the assembly line he will have been thoroughly assessed and the "foreman" will merely have to glance at his card to see the treatment required. In recent years remarkable progress has been made with mechanical, electrical and chemical aids to diagnosis. A delicate machine writes a picture of the heart beats, revealing more than the most skilled specialist could discover with a stethoscope. Another device records blood pressure. The electro encephalograph records the "brain waves" and reveals tendencies towards disturbances such as epilepsy. Chemical tests tell the secrets of the blood. The corpuscles are counted. The spinal fluid is analysed. The trend is to use these "aids to diagnosis" more and more. Indeed, if money were no object, a doctor might well demand that a patient be "given the works" before he would commit himself.

Now, obviously, there cannot be enough doctors, pathologists, and laboratory workers to apply all these tests to every sick person. But it would not be hard to devise an electronic machine which would do it in a matter of seconds. The apparatus would be no more complicated than electronic calculators already in use in industry. The record of the heart beats, the X-ray of the chest, the blood count, the urine test, the "brain wave" record would be pushed out like lightning, or like fortune-telling slips from automatic machines. It would be simple in principle to arrange for a final diagnostic section to scan the records, consider all the possibilities in the form of an electrical integrator machine, and then record the diagnosis. A further few hundred valves and circuits would enable the treatment to be prescribed and handed to the patient.

This is the nightmare of a visit to a doctor's surgery half a century hence. There is no queue, because the electronic doctor is dealing with patients at the rate of one every minute, far more accurately than any qualified human. We pass in front of what resembles an elaborate radar set. Temperature, appearance of the tongue, degree of pain, blood pressure, all the innumerable symptoms that it would take a doctor hours to discover are recorded in a matter of seconds. A card is shot out and we read "Take the mixture three times a day after meals. You need more fresh air and exercise." Such an examination and consultation might cost to-day a great deal in time and money. Only mechanisation in this way would make it possible for a Minister of Health to boast truthfully that "Harley Street treatment" was available to everyone.

This is a dream, unlikely to become reality even if only because doctors have the most powerful trade union in the world and would never allow themselves to be replaced by machines. But it is not impossible and may well arise as the result of specialisation or an increasing dependence upon electrical, chemical and other tests. The "old-fashioned" general practitioner had nothing but his thermometer and stethoscope, but he undoubtedly gave more satisfaction to his patients and cured a great number by his regard for human beings as rather more complex than a collection of atomic particles. To the nurse who said "There is a gastric ulcer in Bed 5" he would have replied indignantly that there was nothing of the kind, but a sick man, anxious about his family in his absence and requiring reassurance as vital as medicine or surgery.

The tendency towards specialisation continues so ruthlessly because no man in a lifetime could keep pace with the amount of knowledge that is being collected. The medical student now has the greatest difficulty in learning in six years enough to enable him to begin his practice of medicine and is probably "specialising" almost before he is qualified. Another twenty years' accumulation of knowledge at the accelerating pace of the present century and the difficulty may become nearly impossible. It may be solved, or solve itself, in one of several ways or by some combination. We might have various grades of doctor and nurse. One does not call in a highly qualified structural engineer to mend a tap washer or a chartered accountant to check domestic grocery bills. A more hopeful possibility is that from the extraordinary amount of knowledge accumulated some generalised theory or theories may simplify matters as did the theories of Newton, Darwin and Einstein in other fields. Or it may be that there will be a reaction in favour of the general practitioner with the thought that confidence and knowledge of character is as important in the relationship between patient and doctor as a blood count or an imposing list of degrees.

The change that is likely to come to medicine in the near future is that of far greater emphasis on "preventive" measures. This tendency is already apparent, although attention is still more concentrated upon the cure and treatment of diseases or symptoms than upon the conditions under which they do not arise. A very striking example is afforded by tuberculosis, a disease which in Britain alone claims thousands of victims a year and causes immense hardship and suffering. In the United States tuberculosis kills forty thousand persons a year, and about half a million are living with the disease. Much elaborate research has been done to find a "cure" for tuberculosis. We spend hundreds of thousands of pounds a year on sanatoriums and surgery. The really astonishing fact is that for many years it has been known that a great deal of tuberculosis is passed on by infected milk, and that if there were no infection of this type the number of cases of tuberculosis would fall rapidly; but it is only recently that we have begun to take steps to insure cleanliness, and it will be many years before all our milk comes from tubercle-free cows. We were obsessed by the need for treating patients and one real cause was neglected. The popular demand is for "free treatment for all," not for conditions which would ensure that the treatment became unnecessary. If our medicine had been organised upon the Chinese system where a doctor is paid for keeping a patient well and loses his fee when the patient becomes ill, the approach to consumption and many other evils might have been different.

Medicine blames every kind of organism for various diseases. In the near future it may concern itself much more with the reasons which seem to direct the intelligence of these organisms to attack specific individuals. Gastric ulcers are a good example and much effort is put into the treatment of this trouble which has become almost an occupational disease of civilisation. In general terms we know the circumstances that produce the condition in one man and not in another, but the emphasis is often upon delicate curative operations rather than prevention. We can even go further. Until comparatively lately doctors have thought of accidents in terms of treatment for broken limbs or burned flesh. It seems to be just realised that to prevent accidents is a more certain way of saving life and health than the patching of broken bodies. A scientific approach to casualties is showing that in spite of their name they often have causes as specific as the bacteria which invade the blood. It is not possible to confer immunity from accidents by injecting a serum, although even this might be successful in the far future if the true cases of "accident proneness" are discovered to represent more than a very small proportion to the total. But the field of medicine is being greatly extended to consider first causes. The virtual disappearance of small-pox in Britain may be due almost as much to improved sanitation and hygiene as to vaccination. Other ailments must be fought in the same way, for this is the only approach which seems to offer any real hope of permanently reducing the terrible variety of illnesses to which man is subject.

To-day, many conditions of ill-health are often attributed to a psychological origin. Asthma, certain types of ulcer and other illnesses originate, it is suggested, in the "mind" or "temperament" and it is well known that there are numerous conditions, from a paralysed limb to loss of speech, which can be due to purely mental causes. It is possible to have a severe headache, as bad as that originally caused by a brain tumour, without any "organic" cause.

The headache is no less "real" because it is imaginary. We are likely to discover in the near future that susceptibility to various troubles and infections can be dependent on the mind. The man who feels depressed, perhaps, catches a cold which, if he were elated, he would escape under exactly similar physical conditions. Unintelligent psychologists are frequently tempted to over-emphasize this aspect of disease and attribute a mental cause to every illness, but the fact remains that very little accurate knowledge has as yet been obtained on this subject.

Medicine has too often concentrated upon what can be seen under the microscope, transferred from rat to rat or revealed by chemical-biological tests, and it is unfortunate that modern psychology should depend so much upon technical phrases that sheer humbug is occasionally able to assure financial success. Causation is very little understood and this new branch of pre-medical disease must be extended until clinical fact replaces prejudiced opinion. The cause, for example, of arterial breakdown is given as certain changes in their structure; more and more laboratories enter into more and more detail, but explanation is seldom offered as to why changes occur in A when they do not in B, although it is this very knowledge that might reveal a real cause. This danger of "laboratory medicine," valuable as it is, has been realised and it may be that some return will take place to the humanities where minds and characters are never forgotten. Apart from difficulties of research on this subject, it is comparatively unrewarding unless the knowledge obtained can be applied without delay. It is so very much easier to alter the chemical reactions of the stomach than to control a temperament with all its inherited conditionings. The patient has been educated to believe more in a bottle of medicine than in good advice.

As we have learned to avoid or to cure common ailments of the body, so we seem to have become more subject to ailments of the mind; our mental institutions are even more crowded than "general" hospitals and mental illness appears to increase in every civilised country. Until a comparatively short time ago insanity in most forms was considered "incurable." Sometimes the sufferers recovered spontaneously, but there was virtually no treatment. A mental hospital was called a lunatic asylum and its chief object was to prevent the sufferers from harming others or themselves. The ancients tried to treat these illnesses in various crude, and as we consider it, barbarous ways, from the snake pit to the suddenly fired pistol which is now replaced by other forms of shock. There was a reaction against this "inhumanity" until lunatic asylums became mere cages, and it is only within the last few years that we have made progress in the treatment or cure of serious mental illness. The first steps were taken as a result of a new outlook upon the human mind put forward in England long before the days of Freud; it suggested that "lunatics" were not to be treated as people cursed by some mysterious disease which rendered them so far apart from the sane, but as men and women with brains that had become disordered. These theories led to the psychological methods of treatment of which orthodox medicine was at first suspicious, but some progress was eventually made by the use of various physical methods to "short circuit" what was often an extremely time-consuming treatment.

In recent years we have seen success from the use of narcotics, electric shock and even surgery for the removal of part of the brain in many cases of mental illness which, not long ago, would have been considered "hopeless." Much of the treatment is empirical and crude in the extreme, but it is effective in a sufficiently high proportion of cases to be justified. In the near future we shall come to a much greater understanding of the brain in action, as distinct from the brain in the dissecting room. We shall be helped by delicate recorders of small electrical charges, developed as a result of discovery and invention in radio. Although the current variations recorded on the electro-encephalograph are called "brain waves" because they have a wave formation, they have, in fact, nothing to do with definite thought as far as we know to-day. The use of this device is still new and the very difficult task of interpreting the changes that occur in the brain under various conditions is still in its infancy. Quite apart from an understanding of the phenomena of sleep and the better diagnosis or location of tumours, the "E.E.G." in new forms is likely to give us much more understanding of mental processes in general.

Already it has shed light upon epilepsy and it is claimed that a tendency to this condition can be detected, even when there are no outward signs, by means of an E.E.G. The importance of this lies not only in greater knowledge and in the development of useful treatment, but in the possibility of reducing the incidence of epilepsy by giving guidance to parents who might unwittingly pass it on to their offspring. Epilepsy is hereditary, but the tendency to it is not always outwardly manifest. If a person with this tendency marries someone with no tendency, the proba-bility is that the offspring will have no strong liability. But if two people, each with this condition, have children, the child with a "double set" may develop the disease. It may be that an E.E.G. test of both parents will soon be considered a sensible preliminary to bringing a family into the world. Other investigations such as the Rh-Factor blood test may also be used in the same way.

Exploration of the living brain by this device and by other techniques now being developed should result in a great improvement in the treatment of mental disease, and the time may not be far distant when the chances of a cure are as high as with any common "organic" complaint. Only a proportion of serious mental diseases are possibly due to actual changes in the tissue which would be as difficult to treat as changes in other vital organs. There is a far better understanding to-day of the causes of mental aberration, and we may hope to see the same progress in this class of preventive medicine as has been made in a "physical" direction. The very great number of men and women whose minds are so delicately balanced that they are likely to be thrown out of gear by small changes in circumstances was shown by psychiatric examinations during the war. There is no way of telling whether these "nervous breakdowns" or disorders are commoner to-day than two centuries ago when they were known by the less technical but very expressive names of "the vapours" and "melancholy."

Indications seem to show that civilisation and industrialisation impose additional stresses on men and women, adding to the risk of mental illness, just as their congregation in towns increases the risk of infectious disease. In the near future we shall adopt methods of "hygiene" for the mind as we have adopted public hygiene for reducing the onset of disease which is due to poor drainage or bad drinking water. The task is much more difficult because everyone resents restraint of mental freedom even more than a ban upon their physical ability to do as they please. Already, by showing that work which is too responsible or not sufficiently responsible may cause a breakdown and by studying the problem of the "square peg in the round hole" from many points of view, the way is being paved to make many more people happy as well as prosperous.

The most spectacular advances in the next decade are likely to be in the realm of surgery. Preventive medicine, whether of the body or the mind, is unspectacular and in rightly acclaiming progress in surgery, such as the so-called "blue-baby" operation, we must not overlook the fact that from the aspect of saving life and giving true health the construction of a new housing estate may do more than a thousand operations. Not that this detracts from the importance of surgery. Until the last few years, for example, surgery of the heart was considered impracticable and as dangerous as was surgery of the abdomen two centuries ago. Now, a number of cardiac conditions are being treated by surgery and this field will rapidly extend. A difficulty in dealing with the heart is that the organ must continue to function throughout the operation. At best the surgeon can have only a moment while the blood supply is interrupted. Now we can reasonably expect the design of a successful artificial heart which would continue the work of circulating the blood while the real heart was being operated upon.

For more than ten years attempts have been made to construct a practical oxygenerator and especially an "artificial heart" in which the blood would be oxygenated and then rhythmically pumped at the proper pressure to the circulatory system. Great technical difficulties have been slowly overcome and it is now claimed that animals have been kept alive for several hours with their hearts "short circuited." The greatest caution will be necessary in using such devices on human beings, but the apparatus is likely to be valuable not only in permitting more extensive surgery but in the avoidance of shock or the possibility of "restoring life" in certain cases of heart failure due to causes other than serious organic breakdown.

In the course of time the collaboration of engineers and medical men may show the way to the production of other artificial organs which will enable the natural parts to be "rested" or operated upon with safety. These devices do not, of course, increase the span of life except in the sense that they enable an individual to survive a particular period during which life might have failed. In the distant future it is conceivable that life might be prolonged by artificial organs replacing or supplementing the natural and that a "heart aid" will become as common as is a hearing aid to-day; that time is far away but it is made all the more interesting by recent successful tests of artificial lungs and kidneys. It has even been suggested that a complete head might be kept alive for short periods after it had been detached from its body.

The question of prolonging life interests all human beings and has received increasing attention from medicine during the past few years. It is noteworthy that all the latest advances of the medical world have not very noticeably added to the span of life. They have merely increased the number of people who reach old age. This explains an apparent increase in the number of cases of certain diseases, especially of the circulatory system, which are liable to attack the aged. Many of those who have been recorded as dying of "heart disease" would, under previous conditions, have succumbed to pneumonia or one of the simple fevers earlier in life. The problem of increasing the total time of living is quite different. In spite of extensive study we have little knowledge of why human beings "wear out." Why do cells lose their ability to renew themselves? Why, in short, do we grow old? In the past there has been much speculation on the subject, but very little scientific research. All kinds of theories have been advanced, from the ingenious idea that death is due to radiation by the normal radio-activity of the earth over the course of seventy years, to suggestions associated with eating, or not eating, almost everything from nuts, grass, meat and cooked food. It is only lately that really extensive research has been carried out. Various interesting discoveries have been made in this science of "geriatrics" and we may soon gain some knowledge as to how senility, or even death, can be postponed. The famous Voronoff operation did not always increase the span of life but was claimed to give vigour and youthfulness for a longer period, in other words, postponing decay. It is possible that if certain glands prove to be the key to the secret, ways will be found of supplying them with the necessary chemicals so that men and women will be able to delay death by injections, as a diabetic holds life together by insulin. The new "cortisone" suggests that steps are already being taken in this direction.

Work on the postponement of old age has become far more important now that the proportion of old persons is rising due to a fall in the birthrate, and a greater survival rate for those in middle age. A society in which one quarter of the men and women had to be supported by the rest because they were "too old" to work might break down under the burden. Given the choice, some would rate better health with mental and physical vigour between the ages of sixty and seventy more important than prolonging the span of life from seventy to eighty, for the "elixir of life" which fascinated mankind centuries ago with its promise of eternal youthfulness is now realised to be a will-o'-the-wisp. Any increase in the term of life, as distinct from the chances of reaching and enjoying old age, will come very slowly. It would be satisfactory, and may come true, that a century hence a lifetime will be regarded as four score years instead of three score and ten.

Quite a number of tests have been made in an attempt to extend the possibilities of grafting as applied to the prolongation of life, but it cannot be said that any real success has been achieved, although it must be remembered that surgery in its technical form is little more than a century old and may soon make progress in these methods. The skill with which ears, noses and lips can now be replaced makes it clear that the art of graft will be enormously extended. Beginning with the simplest forms of membrane it is now not very difficult to build up new faces and claims have been made for replacements of complete limbs in some countries. In the next fifty years advances will be made even more sensational than those which have taken place since the not very distant time when surgeons operated in frock coats which were fashionably covered in dried blood and pus.

We can be certain that legislation must eventually be introduced to control what might become an almost wholesale market in human parts. Ears can now be purchased, the cornea of an eye from a recently dead person is commonly employed to cure certain forms of partial blindness and there is no doubt at all that many more complicated structures will soon be replaceable; we have already blood banks and bone banks and part uterus grafts are entirely successful. The law will also take its part in the control of artificial insemination which is becoming quite a general procedure. It leads to the idea that childbirth itself will be so changed that few of its existing disadvantages will remain. It is also important to notice that a dead man can beget children for a short period after life becomes extinct, a fact which will make changes in the laws of inheritance almost essential.

Another long expected medical advance will be the discovery of methods of securing anaesthesia without the use of ordinary drugs. Great progress has been made since the early days of chloroform which is now seldom used for general purposes, but no "perfect" anaesthetic has been found. The anaesthetist has a considerable range at his disposal, each with its advantages and none without its own restrictions; the drug that secures the unconsciousness and relaxation desired may also over-affect breathing, the heart, or other functions of the body. Hypnotism has been suggested for various minor operations with the advantage claimed that it produces no physiological change and although quite impracticable for ordinary service it is possible that it may lead to some method of electrical brain control. Scientists claim to have produced sleep artificially by the aid of electrical impulses similar to those found in a person who is sleeping naturally. Development of this technique into full anaesthesia might have great advantages for the surgeon and for the patient who would endure none of the unpleasant after-effects experienced with so many chemical anaesthetics.

Of one advance in this direction we can be sure; pain will be regarded with the horror which we have now for operations in the days when no relief was possible. Patients will not be told to be "plucky" or given local anaesthesia while the senses remain to be shocked. Pain indicates failure to know the human body as an entity, a fact which has become well recognised in methods of childbirth now generally adopted in the face of bitter criticism only a few years ago when the experts of church and medicine quoted the biblical reference to "pain and suffering" as a counter to scientific argument.

Ectogenesis is only for the far distant future, if it ever should be available, but some method of relieving women from the disadvantages under which they still suffer is clearly indicated as both sexes become more free to undertake every kind of industrial employment. Constant striving for improvements in the national health will lead us to many novel theories which seem almost fantastic to-day. Special types of food for specific professions have already been suggested and the time cannot be far distant when a whole range of sense-aids comes into being. With all our much vaunted progress in medicine our bodies have not greatly changed in the short time for which we possess any satisfactory record. We retain the characteristic throats of our fish ancestors, we have not even learnt to protect our dwindling frames by clothing that is other than absurd. We are still very close to the savage in every physiological respect.

CHAPTER 7

THE FOOD OF THE FUTURE

IN dealing with the future of medicine little reference has been made to food, although there are many who believe that most of our civilised ills are due to the food we eat and that, eventually, we shall avoid most forms of disease by adopting an improved diet. Every few years during the last century someone has imagined that the "secret" of good health is in the eating, or not eating, of some food or combination of foods. These discoveries have been highly publicised and for a few months or years numbers of people have eaten, or not eaten, the supposed elixirs of life, whether these be honey, milk, meat or salt and in due course another "discovery" has been made which has become the fashion. Scientifically there does not seem to be a shred of evidence that eating or not eating any particular food guarantees good health and long life for everyone. Even the dietetic experts are coming back to the idea that our reasonable preferences are a useful guide and that, except in the case of some particular illnesses, there are no foods that ensure health for all under every condition. The once popular idea that raw and primitive foods possessed some magic is no longer so popular; it is being appreciated that imitating the diet of savages whose lives were usually short is no more logical than copying the diets of animals with different types of stomachs or digestive juices.

Undoubtedly further research will reveal the part played by different foods in promoting normal health. Each year sees its new discovery of some "essential" mineral or vitamin and, if it is valuable, its artificial preparation for use as a "medicine" or a supplement. Some of these substances are valuable and in the second half of the century many conditions of ill-health will be cured as a result of new dietetic discoveries. But, in general, results seem to indicate that to follow the appetite over a wide range of foods is satisfactory and that this is likely to remain so for many years. The human body cannot yet be induced to accept nourishment in tabloid form or be supplied by direct electrical energy for the good reason that its mechanism needs to be exercised by actual bulk. Changes of this kind occupy vast periods of time as is seen in our dwindling hair and teeth which are no longer needed for protection or for the consumption of hard, uncooked food. We encourage, to-day, thought rather than action and seldom respect an individual for his eating capacity or his muscular development.

The great problem of the future may be that of making available this wide range of foods in sufficient quantity.

It is unfortunate that man who has found a method of producing motor-cars, aeroplanes, battleships, and a thousand other complex devices should still be most deeply concerned with the two troubles that must have obsessed his prehistoric ancestors long before the form of Homo sapiens. These twin problems are those of food and shelter, and of the two the more pressing or intractable has always been that of food. The whole life of primitive men and women revolved around food. To-day, many thousands of years later, it is the most popular topic of conversation for millions, many thousands die every year through lack of food and many millions suffer ill-health and premature death through insufficient food.

Even in countries like Britain which have evolved a very elaborate way of life by building up highly efficient and technical industries, the need of sufficient food hangs like a menacing cloud over the population. It is an obvious, but often overlooked, fact that although we have learned to turn coal into a thousand things from aspirins to fertilisers and although we can make drugs and fine fabric from the most unlikely raw materials, we have not managed to make a single ton of food. All our great food industry is based, not on making food, but in turning natural foods from one form into another which is more palatable, saleable, or digestible. For our food we depend wholly upon agriculture and fishing, just as did our ancestors so many centuries ago.

It is because of this truth that we receive so many pessimistic forecasts from experts as to future world supplies. There is no need to detail these forecasts. The essence of all is that while the area of the world is fixed, the population continues to expand, and seems likely to do so at an accelerating rate because of the preservation of life by science, medicine and hygiene. Formerly, our numbers were held static by disease, famine and war. The expansion of population during the last 150 years has been incomparably greater than in the previous 3,000 years and the most striking example, perhaps, has been in India, where there were about 100 million people when the British took charge. This had been the population of India for centuries. In the comparatively short period of British control, the population expanded to about 450 million and is growing at such a speed that, if it continues, those living to-day will see an India with 600 million inhabitants.

Forecasts of famine on a world-wide scale in the rather near future are made on the assumption that population is increasing very much more rapidly than food production and that with an almost fixed amount of food each year to be divided among more and more millions, the share of each must become less. The amount of food may even, it is said, be reduced because in his anxiety to produce cheap food rapidly man has used farming methods that are destructive of the soil which is the source of all our food. Vast new "deserts," such as the dust bowl in the Middle West of America, have been created and, no less important, the fertility of many millions of acres all over the world has been lessened. Erosion has destroyed considerable areas and this, with de-forestation and poor farming, can result in top soil being destroyed and blown away to leave little more than a desert in five or ten years. There is no way of restoring this land quickly, even by the most strenuous effort, for humus is a natural product that takes many years to produce even under favourable conditions. The only alternative to disaster, it is hinted, is for all the nations to join together in the organised production and distribution of food.

While most will agree with this solution in principle, many will be doubtful whether, in practice, a world that has been unable to reach complete agreement on such simple things as copyright and patents is likely to agree on such fundamentals as food production and consumption.

Moreover, food is only one side of the problem; there is the increase in population. Countries asked to make sacrifices to feed others might insist that the underfed countries should not increase their numbers. Would they agree, and would they have the ability to enforce stabilisation even if they agreed in principle? The breeding nations are not those best given to reason.

Proper consideration makes it clear that these forecasts of disaster are founded upon a number of fallacies and that while food may be a preoccupation of the world for centuries to come, the possibility of world-wide and permanent famine is probably less than it has ever been before. There are a number of reasons for this statement and some of them will render obvious what is likely to happen to our food in the future.

Most statistics about failing food supplies in the near future are based upon crude calculations that it requires so many acres to support one man adequately, the usual figure is 2.5 acres, and that an increasing population will have to share in the products of a fixed number of acres. But, in practice, what counts is not the area, but the area fully used for food production. This is a very small proportion of the total area of the land, estimates vary from one-twentieth to one-tenth. Not all the remaining ninety-five or ninety per cent is suitable for food growing, but even to double the area producing food in one way or another would have a remarkable effect on the amount available by our present methods. In the near future we are likely to see large areas which are at present unproductive made to yield food, the vast ground-nuts scheme in Central Africa and the sorghum-growing scheme in Queensland deal with millions of acres of unproductive or not wholly productive soil and are examples of many other projects to bring land into production with results which we shall see in the next few years.

At any given time the area of land available for food

depends upon the technical standard of agriculture. This is improving rapidly. There are certain great territories which are obviously not worth considering for their potential food production, lands where the ground is permanently frozen or where the summer lasts only a month or two, or mountains above the snow line. Even these may one day be considered as a result of technical advances in the control of climate. But there are millions of square miles which would not have been given a moment's thought only fifty years ago, that to-day are reasonable possibilities. The advances which make it feasible to consider such areas for agriculture are many; the invention of efficient insecticides, the production of more powerful earth-working machinery, the developments of new strains of plants able to withstand greater or lesser degrees of heat and cold or to mature more quickly, and the invention of new food processing methods which enable previously unpalatable or unpopular plants to be used.

Sunflower crops from Central Africa are an example of what would have been a small contribution to British food supplies before the invention of margarine with methods of processing vegetable fats to make these crops acceptable. A single scientific discovery can make millions of unproductive acres potentially productive. The development of a method of making animals immune to the disease carried by tsetse flies, or of eliminating the tsetse fly as we have dealt with the malarial mosquito, would make it possible to use hundreds of thousands of square miles of land which is at present infertile.

In India, in Egypt and in many other countries, artificial irrigation has made land of very low productivity yield good crops. There still remain great areas where dams could be built for irrigation, and civil engineering on such a scale becomes more simple each year with the help of improved technique, machinery and special explosives. There is no doubt an even greater area that could become serviceable if drained, for mechanical excavators, bulldozers, atomic fission and new machinery have completely changed our ideas of what is possible. In the next few years the need for more food is likely to see the methods of industry increasingly applied to agriculture; the application of scientific discoveries to food production have been trivial as compared with their application to the factory. A great part of the world's farming is carried out with little more efficiency than that of a century ago and much of it by the methods of the Middle Ages. Even in countries like Britain and the U.S.A. where productivity of the land and the use of manpower have been enormously increased by machines, new plans and new strains of plants and animals, the difference between the best farming and the poorest is still very great. To raise the standards of the worst farms to the standards of the average would mean an enormous increase in food.

A few examples are interesting. The average yield of potatoes is about seven tons to the acre. Good farming can produce over ten tons to the acre. Average dairy farming produces 600 gallons of milk an acre a year, good dairy farming 1,000 gallons. The differences between the standards of the best farmed countries and of the worst is even more striking. Britain, for example, takes over nineteen cwt. of wheat per acre, whereas Australia and Russia have only about five cwt. Raising productivity does not necessarily mean reducing the fertility of the ground. On the contrary, it generally accompanies "good farming." We have been told that in Britain alone it is practicable to produce food for another four million people in five years. Britain is little more than a pin-prick on the map of the world and by the application of science to farming it should be simple for the world to produce the additional food required for the twenty million annual increase in its population.

Some of the developments of the near future directed

towards bringing more land into production and increasing the productivity of land already in use are as follows:—

(1) Far wider use of insecticides and modern methods for controlling diseases and weeds. Animal and insect pests are estimated to destroy sixty-five million tons of grain a year. This is as much bread grain as was required to feed Europe before the war. It is impracticable completely to eliminate this waste, but to avoid even half of it would immensely add to the useful food supply. We have new methods of destroying pests, new synthetic insecticides and new methods of spreading them effectively. The helicopter has proved most valuable in delivering insecticides over large areas with which it would be impossible to deal by hand or even by land machines. For the destruction of insect pests in food in storage we have supersonic devices. The rat continues to be a major problem throughout the world and at best is no more than held in check. But campaigns to reduce the rat population are becoming effective. New poisons and new biological methods of attack will soon be ready and there is a very special benefit to be derived from the destruction of rats which are formidable disease carriers as well as destroyers of food. In this category of development we must place the new synthetic hormones which act as "weed killers." They act selectively, roughly on the principle of stimulating the growth of one plant so rapidly that it kills itself while leaving another unaffected. It is now possible to weed a lawn by spraying it with a hormone preparation to destroy the plants of almost all varieties except those desired. "Weeding" field crops of grain has been impractical, but hormones offer a practical method. Ground before being sown in the future may be treated so that the growth of all plants except those required is inhibited.

(2) The development of improved species and strains of plants and animals. This work has been progressing steadily for more than a century, but the advances made

have been much greater during the present century as the result of our increased knowledge of genetics. It has many aspects, but one of the most important is the evolution of strains of cereals able to withstand extremes of climate. Areas where wheat can be grown are determined by the climate. They do not exactly follow the lines of latitude, but temperature is a very important factor. We know, within limits, how to breed new strains of wheat which will bear rigorous conditions, either because they are able to mature in a very short summer, or to withstand drought or heat or because they can withstand the attack of diseases favoured by damp. In the last twenty years wheat has been grown in areas which previously were quite unsuitable. Scientists will continue to produce new strains of cereal which will enlarge the area that may be cultivated. Only a small change may result in an enormous area being made ready for farming in this way.

These circumstances apply to other food plants. The evolution of new strains giving a heavier yield, or capable of being grown in areas previously unsuitable, will eventually lead to a time when only comparatively small areas of the world will be neglected. The acreage under cultivation is still such that a very small improvement in yield results in a great potential increase of the world's production.

In the case of animals the effort has been made to produce strains and breeds which are increasingly "efficient" from the desired point of view. The wild fowl only lays in spring, perhaps a total of twenty eggs. The domestic fowl which has been evolved from it by careful selection and breeding is now capable of laying 300 eggs a year and laying the majority of them in the autumn and winter, the period when it is against their natural form to do so. They can be helped by providing artificial light. The modern bacon pig is another example for it bears no relation to the wild pig in its ability to provide meat. Cattle have been bred to yield milk so effectively that the yield of the best is double that of the average, itself the product of much selective breeding over the centuries.

Scientific breeders have the ability to mould animals to the special forms that are required as never before. But the process is by no means complete. The "pedigree" herds of animals and flocks of hens are a small fraction of the total in the world. In the next few years while continuing to produce better strains, there will be a renewed effort at consolidation and at raising the average, a task which is greatly assisted by modern transport and research. Artificial insemination means that the best bulls can sire offspring anywhere in the world in great numbers and at small cost, so that the total number of bulls which need be kept is enormously reduced. Eggs from the best strains of hen can be transported anywhere and the standards of flocks improved to a point where the yield can be doubled. Scientists are providing the material. Education and organisation must ensure that the best use of it is made.

(3) New machinery will raise the yield of food that can be obtained with the same amount of labour. The application of machinery to farming has been one of the great revolutions in agriculture, but it is only in its infancy. The tractor springs immediately to mind, although it is only one form of farm machinery. It very much reduces the manpower required to cultivate an acre; yet a great part of the world's farming is still carried out by primitive methods with oxen, or even human beings, harnessed to the plough. The number of tractors in Britain is 250,000 and it is estimated that with 300,000 the need would be completely filled. This "target" is likely to be reached in a few years, but it would be absurd to imagine that this means the end of farm mechanisation or economy in manpower.

It is only in recent years that we have begun to use machines for many old-fashioned operations and the next twenty years will see a revolution in farming as great as that introduced by the mechanical reaper or the "combine" reaper and thresher. There are machines for lifting and planting potatoes, machines for planting every sort of seedling from cabbage to strawberries, machines for spreading manure and machines for harvesting and preparing sugar beet. There is no farm work from "hedging and ditching" to fruit picking that cannot be mechanised and it is only by mechanisation that the farmer can obtain the higher productivity that will give the farm worker and owner the improved standard of living which is now demanded. In the near future we shall see greater production from the land with no greater labour force; farming without men. This will have far-reaching social and economic consequences and we have had a glimpse of the future from the results of the invention of successful cotton picking machines in the U.S.A.; cotton picking had for a century been the work of the lowly paid Negro. It is safe to say that there is now no farm work for which the engineer cannot devise a machine. Whether and when the machine comes to be extensively used as is the tractor and the electric milker, depends upon the speed of capital investment and the extensiveness of the operation to be performed. A strawberry picker would have to be very simple to prove worth-while because it would be used only on a few days a year on limited crops. Last, but not least, we depend upon finding a remedy for the natural conservatism of the land worker; but as an example of the ingenuity of the latest farm machines may be quoted a "tree-shaker" which knocks nuts off a tree and then sucks them up by vacuum.

Many farming operations are traditional rather than efficient. It is, for example, now widely accepted that the best use of grass is made if it is treated as a food crop. But the ancient method of haymaking, in which losses of food value due to the vagaries of the weather may be enormous, is still practised. In the future, the hay harvester will probably become as common as is the combine reaper to-day. The harvester cuts the grass, chops it and carries it to a wagon behind from which it is mechanically unloaded into dehydrators. Within hours the grass has become a dry food, with no loss of its protein or vitamins. The universal adoption of this or some similar method of "hay-making" would alone, over the whole world, result in sufficient additional nourishment being available to feed hundreds of thousands of livestock.

These are only a few cases of how machines will make it possible for even the existing cultivated land to yield a greatly increased amount of food at a reasonable cost. The majority of the world's farmers use tools and methods which suggest that the industrial revolution, certainly the electrical revolution, has completely passed them by. A demand for food will provide the incentive and opportunity for vast changes. Mechanisation will mean bigger and fewer farms or at least larger units. The forty-acre farm is no more suitable for mechanisation than is a small garage "factory" for mass production.

With bigger farms will come an opportunity to use the aeroplane, possibly with radar control, to a greater extent. The speed with which aircraft can work exceeds that of the land machine by more than the speed of the tractor exceeds that of the horse. Seed sowing, insecticide dusting and certain other work can be carried out from the air, particularly when helicopters are employed. The special advantage of the aeroplane is speed. Favourable conditions for seed sowing may exist for only a few days. In this time an aeroplane could sow thousands of acres. In the same way, an attack on infestation must be rapid to be fully effective. Mechanical sprays from the ground might cover the affected area in the course of a week, but an aeroplane would deal with the same area in a single day and thus immensely reduce the loss. For these specialised purposes in suitable areas the hired helicopter will prove of great value to farming.

There is the probability of a huge increase in food production in the world by improved farming technique and there is also the hope that a great deal of additional food will be produced without farming. There are three chief ways in which this will be done. They have all been tried experimentally, some have passed the experimental stage, but none makes at the moment any great contribution to the world's supply. The extent to which they are developed is a matter of economics and the three methods can roughly be defined as the production of palatable and digestible food from "animal feeding stuffs," the harnessing of plants to produce food without the use of soil and the production of food from inorganic materials.

First, the production of foodstuffs from wheat which otherwise might be considered fit only for animal feeding already takes place on a considerable scale. Margarine, the chief fat supply for many millions in industrial countries, is a "synthetic" foodstuff in that its raw materials would not be considered palatable or even edible. The invention of margarine made it possible to use animal fats and vegetable oils which at best could only have made a very indirect contribution to our foods by being fed to animals which would later be eaten. Hydrogenation makes it easy to turn oils into a form which is more palatable and nutritious. Various so-called "synthetic" foods have now been made; there is one, for example, which has been manufactured on a considerable scale from yeast. The yeast is "fed" with sugar which turns it into a substance containing protein that can be made thoroughly palatable by processing.

The shortage of food is rarely absolute; it is usually of certain elements in food, particularly the proteins which are normally obtained from meat, fish, cheese; and of vitamins. A shortage of vitamins can generally be remedied by synthetic products, treatment of margarine makes it as rich in vitamins as butter, and our bread has synthetic substances added to improve its nutritive value. What scientists have been aiming at, therefore, is the production of protein-rich foods from second-rate or even waste materials. This is not, strictly, "synthetic" food, but "ersatz." Many of these foods have been produced, one in Germany, for example, in which the ingredients include soya, yeast, and cereals. This is said to have the same dietetic value as meat and to cost about half as much. We shall certainly see a great many more of these "factory foods" in the future. The discovery of a way in which substances like cellulose could be converted into digestible food, even for animals, will be of great importance, for cellulose occurs abundantly. The chemist may show the way in which we could eat our hedge clippings and forests, but a great deal of further research is necessary. We do not yet know the precise differences between all natural and synthetic substances and there are cases where, for no known reason, there may be gaps in nutrient value which are very important.

The basis of all our food is plants, and for a great part of it we have to depend upon animals to turn indigestible plants into digestible meat or milk. It is an inefficient method because in the process of converting grass into milk or meat, a cow wastes a great deal; extra food is required for its own growth and energy. If we could use the grass for direct production there would be an enormous saving in food, for the proportion that reaches us via the cow is comparatively small. There are people who eat grass and claim to thrive on it, but human beings, not having double stomachs, are not normally suited to deal with grass. We must look to the scientist to devise methods by which machines can turn grass into milk, machines which will not be "fuelled" by the grass as is the cow, but by energy produced from coal, itself largely a tree product, or some other inedible fuel. It remains, perhaps, to be discovered if fresh foods contain substances which are essential. The famous case of fish in artificial sea water, and of dogs breathing air from which rare gases had been extracted, will be remembered. Both fish and dogs suffered severely for reasons still obscure; a fact which should encourage humility in all science.

The second method in which food supplies will be increased is by producing plants without intervention of the soil. One obvious way is the system of gardening known as "hydroponics," the substitution of water in which minerals are dissolved, for soil. The process by which atoms of phosphorus, nitrogen, calcium, carbon and many other elements are rearranged in the soil and with the aid of moisture, sunshine and air turned into living tissue, is extremely complex and not yet fully understood. During recent years the importance of minute amounts of certain elements, such as magnesium, in the healthy growth of plants has been discovered but much remains to be learned. Sufficient is known to make it possible to grow plants over tanks containing solutions of the necessary elements. Hydroponics has certain advantages, notably complete control over the growth of the plant and full utilisation of the nutritive chemicals; undoubtedly in normal soil farming a large percentage of the fertilisers applied are wasted. Equally, it has great limitations. It cannot yet be made economical for bulk crops, such as cereals, and is likely to be confined to market gardening. Considerable success has been achieved with selected vegetables in certain parts of the world and there is likely to be some expansion of the method, particularly on barren islands and in population centres far removed from fertile agricultural areas.

The type of farming without soil which is now causing special interest is of a different kind. It is aimed at harnessing very simple plant growths so that with the aid of nutritive elements in the sea and abundant sunshine, they will multiply rapidly and provide bulk food that can be treated to make it edible. The process by which a blade of grass uses a small amount of mineral matter and air and, under the sun, turns it into living tissue, is called photosynthesis. Exactly how the change operates has been one of the major mysteries of science, but there has never been any question that it is the basic process in the production of all food. The fish we eat have derived their nourishment from the smallest organisms in the sea which carry out photosynthesis over millions of square miles, using sunlight to turn the dissolved minerals into the organic material which eventually becomes protein, fat, carbohydrate and vitamins. The exact nature of photosynthesis remains a partial mystery, but within the last two or three years, using "tracer atoms" from atomic piles, we have learned enough to believe that the process can be used by deliberately breeding the living organisms which carry it out.

We may expect to see the first factory for this purpose very shortly, probably in California or some other convenient place where there is plentiful sunshine. The method of operation implies that water will first be taken from the sea and sterilised. It will then have added to it the chemicals necessary for the growth of plants. A small amount of microscopic plankton will be introduced and the water pumped through coils exposed to sunlight. In the coils the plankton will multiply very rapidly, using sunlight to take up the chemicals in the water. Finally, the water will be centrifuged to collect the plankton, too small to be filtered out by ordinary methods. The plankton will be pressed into a food rich in protein which can be used for feeding either men or animals. A continuous-process plant would be able to produce many tons a day. The cost would be relatively low and skilful designing will make it still less when the sterilisation can be carried out by heat obtained on the exchange principle. The gathering of these organisms to produce fat and protein makes it possible to visualise a world food supply that is limited only by our capacity to construct factories and to provide the necessary nutrient elements. The latter are both common and cheap.

The third method of making food would be by true synthesis. Sugar consists only of carbon, hydrogen, nitrogen and oxygen, all elements which occur abundantly on the earth and in the air. The same is true of most of our foodstuffs. They consist of combinations of common elements. The problem is to arrange these elements into the complex molecules of our food. Sugar has been made from coal-tar products by synthesis, but where the more elaborate molecules of fat and protein are concerned we have so far failed. A piece of bread may consist of nothing more than a few trillion atoms of oxygen, nitrogen, carbon and hydrogen moistened by water, but given the atoms, we cannot make the loaf. The work has to be done for us by plants and the process described is one way of using them, more economical, perhaps, than helping their growth on the soil as animal foodstuffs.

The real step forward will come when we master the technique of carrying out in a factory all the processes for which at the moment we are dependent upon animals and there is little doubt that this will happen. It will mark progress not only as decisive as the synthesis of urea, but the end of a fear of world starvation. With huge factories able to produce from air, water and such common minerals as coal, all the fats, sugars, carbohydrates and proteins we need, the danger of famine could not for countless years be due to our inability to provide sufficient food.

At present these ideas may appear fanciful, but they are no more strange than the atom bomb would have seemed only twenty years ago; and they are based on research carried out as a result of the atom bomb itself. A sum similar to that now devoted to atomic research for military purposes would undoubtedly provide the beginnings of these food factories in a few years. The fantastic picture of miles of coils soaking in the sunshine is no more peculiar than the miles of plant actually engaged in producing fissionable material.

It is not suggested that agriculture will become unnecessary, for in the first instance an increase in farm productivity by the methods outlined is of great importance. But to provide cheap and plentiful food for the world's population, factories may be an essential part before the end of the twentieth century and they will make forecasts of "inevitable" starvation seem as foolish as those of Malthus when he also underestimated the world's capacity to produce food as fast as it was needed by its ever-increasing numbers.

One further point must again be emphasised. In our present state of evolution the mechanism of the body must be used as well as nourished. Not for countless centuries can we reach the happy time when food can be taken in tabloids or electronically while we sleep. But the total bulk may be diminished in view of the waste to which our bodies give rise, and there is the additional hope that in the far future we shall discover how to feed specific requirements more exactly. It is absurd that to-day we can make little distinction between the meals given to poets and those upon which engineers may usefully feed.

CHAPTER 8

WAR IN THE FUTURE

FOR many millions the great question mark of the future is summarised by the word "war." Their general attitude is either that war is inevitable and will certainly end civilisation as we know it, or that it is "unthinkable." Both these points of view are exaggerated and are probably based on the fact that so many people have had experience of two major wars in the course of a single generation. It should be realised that, far from "ending civilisation," these two wars with their ghastly toll of life and material have left parts of the world far richer than might have been expected by any prophet writing in 1900.

The mere mention of war as something which is bound to happen may seem disappointing although it is likely at least two or three wars will be raging at the time. But the idea that the normal state of man has been peaceful and that wars have been occasional interruptions to progress is not borne out by history. It would be difficult to find any period of ten years together during the last 2,000 years during which no war was being fought, just as it would be impossible to name half a dozen treaties out of the thousands made between nations that have not been broken within fifty years of being so solemnly signed. Within easy memory there have been a dozen wars, the two "great wars" being merely those involving nations of high industrial potential, distinguished from "minor" wars, in which millions perished, more by the weapons used than by any difference in mental outlook. This is more than cynical comment. It is important that we should be concerned with facts as well as ideals and there is a certain comfort for the future in the thought that the human race has survived an almost continuous condition of strife.

When asked if it would not be a good thing to "abolish war," we should remember that we have already abolished it several times. The years between the two world wars were filled by the comings and goings of statesmen with their pacts to do away with war and the signing of "peace pledges" by citizens who really meant what they said. When the time inevitably came, the battles, for vegetable and animal nature is always at war, were fought with unabated vigour. We must recognise that man is combative and that he will fight even if he realises it is to the death; even if it suggests the destruction of his country or his race. We are anxious that war should end just as we hope that aircraft will never crash. To prevent air disasters it is useless to agree that accidents will not happen or that it is "unnatural" for engines to fail or pilots to make mistakes. Better to face the truth that both these things can occur and to take precautions to the best of our ability.

One argument frequently put forward to explain why there will never be another war, an argument most popular when the fighting is not in Europe, is that modern weapons are so destructive that any future war must mean the end of civilisation. The atomic bomb is such a terrible weapon it is suggested that it will be the "weapon to end war." This amusing idea is not new, it was given by Fulton in support of his submarine 150 years ago and long before that as a final objection to gunpowder. The submarine would be such a threat that it would end naval warfare. A hundred years later it was being "proved" that the destructive power of modern machine guns was such that no army could survive and that wars, if they were fought, would be finished in a few days. Then it was poison gas, it will be remembered, that by its terror was to end all conflict. The theory of the "weapon to end war" has always been false in the past and there is no reason to suppose it will not prove equally ridiculous in the future.

That wars will end because, under modern conditions, there can be no "victor," is likely to survive experience no better. At the end of the nineteenth century a Russian banker gave years to the study of war in all its aspects and produced eight volumes which "proved," among other things, that in future wars there could be no victors, because the winning side would find itself as impoverished as the conquered and unable to recover by its conquests. The facts and the logic were unexceptionable, but wide knowledge of them did not prevent the war of 1914-18 or an attempt to make the conquered "pay." The complete failure of this plan, while the victors threw millions of good money after bad, did not prevent another major war with exactly the same situation recurring. It would be unreal to suppose that these circumstances will never occur again. Like a man who marries again after his third divorce, a nation is always ready to believe that "this time it will be so different."

Quite probably, next time it will be all too "different," in many ways. War has become so complex and technical that the danger of what we must call "civilised warfare" breaking down under its own weight cannot be overlooked. The sums spent by nations to-day on the means of defence are unprecedented, measured either by absolutes or by percentages of national productiveness, and the indications are that these costs must increase if the race for "security" by armament continues. The proportion of the national effort given to preparation for war means lowering the standard of living, and one of the details generally overlooked is that in the comparatively near future the cost and complication of the weapons considered necessary to survival may become such that they will cause the whole economic structure to fail. This might have advantages. One is reminded of certain prehistoric animals which, in the course of evolution, became so overladen with offensive and defensive weapons that they were immobilised, became inefficient organisms and fell easy victims to other species which lacked their tremendous armoury. We must not carry the comparison between animals and human societies too far, but it seems that one way in which the kind of war we know may disappear in the near future is by highly industrialised nations devoting so much of their effort to military ends that they become economically rotten and, in spite of their weapons, collapse before others industrially and technically less developed, but economically much more balanced. The cost of producing and maintaining extremely elaborate weapons might become such that a nation was "ruined" and, when the time came, incapable of using its products effectively.

This is not a fanciful picture. The military mind works in narrow channels. "Defence" is one of the subjects, like religion, upon which human beings seem incapable of thinking scientifically. Any absurdity is acceptable to a country at war provided that it is presented emotionally. "The nation is in danger" has proved a useful cry to politicians for centuries. Fear is one of the most powerful emotions, capable of producing in human beings and human societies results far more peculiar than those attributed to the ostrich with its head in the sand.

At present, there is nothing to suggest that the great industrialised nations will all give up their sovereignty in favour of some international council which alone would control a military force. Even if this came about, it would be necessary for this body to develop its fighting services and weapons in accordance with the latest discoveries. Otherwise, it would in due course find that the "might" which was its supreme right had passed to some other organisation. We must, therefore, examine how weapons and war are likely to change in the coming years.

Since the beginning of war the main trend of development has been to increase the range between combatants. The first primitive weapons gave way to the thrown stone, the club and the spear. Next came artificial aids to propulsion to increase range by bows, catapults, and slings. There followed propulsive explosives which have become progressively more powerful and, most recent development of all, the rocket missile carrying its own engine. The range at which it has been possible to throw missiles at the enemy has increased from a few yards to thousands of miles. At the same time there has been the tendency to increase and to speed up the mobility of combatants. On land, the three or four miles an hour at which soldiers could march has given way to thirty, forty and even sixty miles an hour. At sea, speed has risen from four or five miles an hour when the wind was in the right quarter, to forty miles an hour, whatever the weather conditions. And, of course, air transport has made it practicable to carry men and explosives for thousands of miles in a few hours.

These tendencies must continue; both range and speed are now rapidly approaching the point where they will be too much for the unaided human brain to control. The weapons of the future will be of the kind we popularly call "push-button weapons," depending for their aiming and use upon electrical devices working with the velocity of light instead of the comparative slowness of the human nervous system. It takes about a fifth of a second for the brain, responding to the eyes, to send a message to the muscles of the fingers or feet. That is a very short time, but during that fraction of a second guided missiles can travel hundreds of feet. With fighters and bombers approaching speeds of 700 m.p.h. and likely to reach 1,000 m.p.h. or very much more, the point is being reached where under the most favourable circumstances they would come within range of each other for only a fraction of a second. Increases in speed will make the period of contact so brief that the human hand and eye alone will be useless.

Electronic devices work "instantly," the speed of light and electricity is about 186,000 miles per second, so that the reflection of a light or radar image can be received, dealt with by complex calculating circuits, and made to fire a gun or release a missile in less than a thousandth of a second. The fighter pilot of the future will be guided by radar to the neighborhood of the plane he is seeking to intercept, and he may fire on it without ever having seen it at all. He will have to move a small lever, like the pre-selector gear of a car, and his guns will be set to fire at any object that crosses their sights within range. The gunsight will "see" the target and release its projectiles automatically.

Strange as this may seem, it is only a logical development of apparatus already in existence: radar, the photo-
electric cell and the proximity fuse. The human brain
had, to an appreciable degree, already been eliminated
towards the end of the last war. Without the range-finding and calculating devices that did away with the human
element, anti-aircraft fire would have been quite ineffec-
tive. The considerable fire power of super-fortresses which
enabled them to be used in daylight, depended upon
electronic calculators which were able automatically to
take into account the score of factors required in aerial
gunnery, and make all the correct calculations or allow-
ances. Even with the help of the most elaborate calculating tables, a gunner could not have made the necessary
calculations in time for them to be of any use.

The next step will be for weapons to be aimed and fired
without any kind of human intervention. In many cases
the weapons will be fired by the targets themselves. This
was virtually the case with the proximity-fused shell fired
from anti-aircraft guns. Radar signals from the shell are
reflected back by the target and when the shell and target
are in the right proximity, the fuse is actuated. But the
proximity fuse is useful only if the shell is travelling near
the target. If the shell is not correctly aimed to pass near
the target, its proximity fuse is useless. To compete
with the high speeds of the future we shall have the development of "homing" devices, in which the target itself
acts as a guide and attracts the missile, as a magnet attracts
steel. The "homing" will possibly be based on heat, light
or changes in the magnetic field, according to the nature
of the target. An aircraft attacking another aircraft might
release missiles which will "home" by radar, the varying
strength of the reflected radar signals actuating the steer-
ing device of the missile so that it constantly approaches
its target. It would be possible to make missiles which
"homed" on any shadow; the anti-aircraft missile would

be released in the general direction of an approaching air-craft, would pick up its "shadow" by a sensitive photo-electric cell and then "home" on it as if the bomb carried a photograph of whatever it was required to attack.

Homing devices will also be used on bombs both for attack and defence; they will be fitted on long range missiles. The heat from a large factory would be sufficient to guide a bomb towards it and the warmth from a large city might provide the signal for a missile fired from a great distance. It is feasible, at least theoretically, to measure the heat of a candle at a distance of thousands of miles. Perhaps instead of having to "blackout" lights it will be necessary to douse all fires and to provide camouflage heating towed by aircraft. At sea, there is nothing new in the target-finding torpedo, for it was tested in World War I and the magnetic field of a ship is now sufficient to give the homing signal to yet another type of missile. Any change of course to avoid the auto-matic torpedo would be followed by a change of course of the torpedo itself. There is the further possibility of hom-ing signals, resembling those used to guide civil aircraft, being generated by "fifth columnists." It would be neces-sary to have only a very small transmitter to act as a final guide to the missile fired thousands of miles away. These "suitcase transmitters" might well be planted at important points by spies before the outbreak of hostilities.

To the gunner of Nelson's day the idea of firing a gun at a target twenty miles away, with such accuracy that salvoes could be certain of a hit, would have seemed ridiculous. Aids to range-finding and gun-laying, taking into account the movements of the ship, have made this possible. In fact we can now go one better. It is not neces-sary even to see the target; its direction and range can be found by radar while it is still invisible to the gun-layer. Future developments will be equally striking, and before we jump too hastily to the conclusion that this means the end of warfare because the destruction will be so great, we must remember that defence has always kept pace with attack.

The defence against the "homing" anti-craft missile may take the form of providing "dummy" targets, as the bomber, to a degree, protects itself against radar by dropping large quantities of metallic strips. Homing long distance missiles and bombs will be decoyed so that they land where they do no harm. Large towns might attempt to protect themselves against missiles homing on light or heat by building decoy factories at a few miles distance, in much the same way as lights are used to deceive aircraft into unloading their bombs. It is impossible to think of a weapon, however ingenious, against which, given time, no defence can be devised.

The homing torpedo may be "taken in charge" by its target and either directed to pass by harmlessly or to return to its point of launching. Any missile which is guided by radio offers the possibility of being taken under control by the target which, in the nature of things, must eventually be nearer the missile than the point of control and therefore able to give more powerful signals. We can visualise whole countries, certainly "target areas," enclosed in a radar network so that when this was penetrated by a missile or enemy aircraft, the signals would "trigger" defensive measures.

It is true that, "given time," the defence to any attack will be found. The vital point is how much time is required, for in modern warfare a victory might be won before the defence became effective, as was very nearly the case with both the German V1 and V2 weapons. Because of this, it is extremely important to anticipate new forms of attack. They may not be "practicable." There were experts convinced that the German long-range rockets were not "practicable" even after some of them had landed in London. It is safer to credit the enemy with the ability to produce any weapon that is theoretically possible and to have counter-measures ready. The magnetic mine, the acoustic mine, flying bombs and rockets could all have been predicted with some exactness by any competent and imaginative engineer in 1939. He might not have been able to build them but he could have stated that, given the overcoming of a few technical difficulties, these were possible weapons. Anticipation would have saved some of the great losses they inflicted before effective defensive measures were introduced. War Departments in the future may find it necessary to have "Anticipation Committees" whose task it will be to discover the possibilities based on the latest theoretical knowledge and to forecast the use to which they might be put by any intelligent enemy. There were many instances in the war of 1939 where new suggestions were brushed aside by prejudice only to find later that the principles involved had been employed by the enemy. Magnetic mines and fire-proof petrol tanks are two notable examples.

Warfare has become "total" in the sense that every possibility of scientific discovery and technical invention must be studied from a military point of view and no activity of the enemy can be considered immune from attack. The tendency, indeed, is to concentrate the major weight of attack on the enemy's economic resources rather than on his military forces for the good reason that armed forces have become so large and their weapon equipment so complex that the dependence on industry has enormously increased. Centuries ago, two or three arsenals were sufficient to keep an army in the field and it could live largely "off the land." To-day, variations of weapons and supply are such that ten men are required to plan and manufacture for every one in the field; no army, air force, or navy can move without its vast supporting train. Attack on the source of the weapons and equipment rather than on the men who use them is favoured, not because it is on "unarmed civilians who cannot defend themselves," but because it is the logical way of destroying the armed forces; destroy the heart, and the arms and legs cease to be a danger. The lesson of Japan who surrendered before a single enemy soldier had landed on her territory and with immense armies in the field has, no doubt, been absorbed by every military student in the world. Civilians, men, women and almost children, support an army today; it is just that they should suffer alike.

We must expect, therefore, that many new weapons designed to destroy an enemy's industry and agriculture rather than his fighting men will become of first importance. In the past, battles, even whole campaigns, have been decided by the weather. In the future we may attempt to change the weather, not so much with the idea of engaging an army, although an artificial storm in the path of an advance might have as decisive an effect as to destroy an enemy's economy. Great progress in control of the weather has been made since the 1939 war ended. Results are still very localised, but it has been shown that it is possible to control rainfall or even to produce artificial snow and fog to some extent. A few U.S. experimenters claim considerable success by the use of chemicals, such as solid carbon dioxide or iodine combinations and in the future it may be possible to alter the rainfall of a limited area with some certainty over considerable periods.

Drought does not have to be absolute to produce famine. Reduce the rainfall over certain areas of Britain by half and the economic effect would be more disastrous than many air raids. An opposite effect, the condensation of rain clouds, might produce serious flooding, either locally for putting an airfield out of action, or, of long duration to destroy whole tracts of the countryside. When we consider the "natural floods" and see how comparatively little is required to tip the balance between security and the reverse, the idea of harming a country's production or transport by flooding does not seem entirely academic.

Promising as the experiments have been from a military standpoint, the final decision upon meteorological weapons will depend upon their overall efficiency. It might prove that the same resources devoted to the production of aircraft, long distance missiles or some more orthodox weapon, would give greater results. One of the more strange suggestions sent to the War Office in World War II was that clouds should be "frozen" so that enemy aircraft concealed in them would be brought down. In 1944 this was, of course, utterly impracticable; we do not know how to freeze clouds. But the real point is that even if we had this knowledge, the cost, in manpower and materials, would be far greater than that of many thousands of anti-aircraft guns on the ground which would, at least, have an equal chance of success. This question of efficiency is often overlooked although the possibility of meteorological warfare cannot be omitted from any modern plans.

Since the end of 1940 great strides have been made in the development of biological warfare; the destruction of human beings, animals and plants by biological agents of various types. Research has indicated that the threat from this weapon may be as great, perhaps greater, than that of nuclear fission. The production of biological agents does not require the expenditure of thousands of millions of pounds on factories. It needs only the services of a comparatively small number of experts working in a laboratory with equipment which could easily be provided. Biological weapons could be produced by the smallest nation, with the help of trained biologists, bacteriologists, doctors and chemists. True, the agents have still to be "delivered" on the targets, by bombs, sprays, or missiles, and although this implies the existence of air power these weapons are singularly suitable for use by saboteurs. It would be necessary to place comparatively small amounts

in reservoirs and food storage plants for the deadly work
to begin. It might be some weeks before the nation at-
tacked realised that the attack had been made, even longer
before it could satisfy itself by whom it was threatened.
Bacteriological materials could be easily transported,
whereas the idea of the "commercial traveller carrying a
suitcase" planting an atomic bomb in a big city has to be
ruled out at the moment, because of the weight and bulk
of the bomb. The customs officials would, to put it mildly,
be suspicious. But this disadvantage does not apply to the
bacteria bomb.

The great majority of deadly diseases have been found,
for one reason or another, to be unsuitable for use in warfare. Cholera, for instance, can be too easily stopped by
immunisation and sanitary precautions. Bubonic plague,
with which the Germans experimented before the war, is
spread by fleas and rats; apart from the uncertainty there
is the possibility that the rats might cross frontiers to
spread the disease everywhere. There remain a number
of organisms proved under test to be suitable for spreading by air; the U.S. War Department some time ago listed
thirty-three, including the virus of psittacosis or parrot
fever. This is very virulent. The disease was contracted
by about one-fifth the staff engaged in a laboratory studying its effects even though some had never been in direct
contact with the cultures. Another "possible" is the
botulinus toxin, one of the most deadly forms of food
poisoning.

Pre-war research into the opportunities for bacteriological warfare, both from an offensive and defensive
point of view, suggested that it would not be effective because of the great advances made in immunization and
sanitation. No bacteria dropped from the air into reservoirs could be more deadly than that already in the
water drawn from some rivers; ordinary filtering and puri-
fication processes would deal with them at once. But it is

believed that great "advances" have been made since then, including the production of new diseases by applying radio-activity to existing organisms so that mutations are caused. These new organisms might be made to produce virtually new diseases with new symptoms and be less susceptible to immunisation. Some effects might not even be recognised until an epidemic was in full swing.

All this sounds very terrible and explains why a number of people have said that bacteriological warfare is a greater menace than atomic bombing. Their fears are increased by the ease with which attacks could be made on domestic animals and plants. The world loses millions of tons of food each year by the attack of micro-organisms in spite of the application of all types of spray and the breeding of immune varieties of plants. The deliberate introduction of new harmful organisms with the idea of destroying food might have even more devastating results than an attack on the people. The spreading of an organism to neighbouring countries is not likely to inhibit this method of warfare if the necessary bacteria could be introduced to enemy land by sea or air. All war will be "total" in the future and it would be considered an excellent plan to trap migrating birds and infect them to carry some deadly disease into the country where their flight was to end.

The use of biological agents is something for the future, no large scale tests have even been made. Experiments are now taking place, not as a mere possibility but as something which, like gas, will certainly be used if it proves efficient. The case compares with that of meteorological warfare; it might not be desirable or, for a time, it might prove too troublesome to control. Germ attack is more likely to be used by an enemy on the verge of defeat or with nothing to lose than by an aggressor seeking to conquer territory or peoples, and it may be that the very real threat of the weapon proving a boomerang of death to friend and foe alike will make any nation hesitate. At the same time it is true that every development resulting from research in this field is likely to bring immediate good as well as future danger. If nations became really alarmed on the subject of bacteriological warfare and spent on the scale adopted for atomic research, they might well make discoveries that would eliminate the risk of many infectious diseases for ever. Even as a result of the comparatively small amount of defensive work already carried out, important advances have been made in immunology which are of immediate practical value. The "user" nation would certainly develop its own system of protection before commencing any attack of this character.

There is another class of weapon which must soon be considered as possible. Poison gas is virtually out of date. The gases of World War I were not used in World War II because it was thought that they would not "pay," and although new gases of an "improved" type have been found there is no doubt that defences against them will be evolved. But atomic fission can result in the production of quantities of highly radio-active dust which, used as such, might prove very much more efficient than poison gases or atomic bombs. A comparatively small amount might neutralise a considerable area for weeks, perhaps years. The U.S. Senate were told that U.S. scientists had been experimenting with spreading "clouds" of radio-active dust so potent that a single shell would make a square mile deadly to anyone entering it, also that experiments had been conducted with radiating poison gases so that they would be poisonous even if gas masks were worn; radiations from the gas would pass through concrete walls and bring slow death to anyone near.

Radio-activity is almost a "perfect" poison from the military aspect. It can be spread from comparatively small missiles; it is odourless, tasteless and invisible. It can be detected with great efficiency by Geiger counters but it is not easy to secure immunity, even with special clothing, and it is extremely persistent. Radio-activity might be found still dangerous a year later. It is particularly easily spread by water, a single small bomb of radio-active material in a reservoir would make the water dangerous to anyone who drank it, and although the radiation could be detected it could be eliminated only by special elaborate and expensive filtering systems. This affinity for radiation is such that it might not be necessary to drop atomic bombs on any city near water. It would be sufficient to drop the bomb in the water, the sea, a river or a lake. An improved radio-active spray from the bomb could envelop the city and bring death to anyone who remained although modern defence methods are rapidly catching up with this problem.

This brings us to the whole question of atomic weapons. These are necessarily difficult to describe because of the secrecy that surrounds research, but there are a number of points that can be made as to the use of atomic fission. The effect is extremely powerful compared with any explosives and it is that which makes the bomb so spectacular. We can say that one bomb is the equivalent of a raid by 1,000 large bombers armed with T.N.T.; but it is not the same. The effect is more concentrated and more lasting. Some of the far-reaching effects forecast after Hiroshima may not have proved true, but it must be remembered that the Hiroshima bomb was dropped to explode at a height which would increase the distant effects of blast, heat flash and radiation while minimising the long-period effect of lingering radio-activity. It is now probable that bombs could be dropped to produce not only immediate destruction but the "neutralisation" of a wide area for some time ahead. It is because the 1939 war showed that physical destruction, however great, could be made good, that this lasting effect appeals so strongly to the strategist. Atomic bombs and missiles could be used in creating radio-active obstacles in the path of an enemy rather than in direct attacks upon well defended targets. A single bomb, exploded in the right way, is capable of creating a radio-active "desert" of several square miles which it would be highly dangerous to enter and atomic bombs might be used for creating such areas at vital points in which enemy forces could be pinned down.

The fitting of atomic warheads to long-distance rocket missiles presents a problem which will shortly be solved, but now that all types of travelling bombs can be guided and thus attain very much greater accuracy, it may be considered wasteful to employ in them atomic "explosives," of which the supply is limited. In the light of our present knowledge, although the weight of fissionable material is small, the container with its "fusing" arrangements is bulky and it seems unlikely that it will be possible to use fission bombs from very small weapons without a good deal of experiment. The energy is far too violently released and too uncontrolled for a propellant, so that cordite, T.N.T. and the other explosives may continue to serve for guns or small shells. Rocket missiles will probably be propelled by liquid fuels and there is reason to believe that liquid explosives may replace the usual type of propellant in the ordinary gun. High speed fire will be applied to the larger type of weapon and there are likely to be methods of automatically setting fuses while shells are actually moving in the gun-barrel or, in the case of rockets, while in flight.

Although future major wars will be fought at great distances and it is difficult to conceive of a battlefield much smaller than the whole world, armies will still have the task of occupying territory and we must expect the development of new weapons for this purpose. The tendency may be towards small, highly mobile, striking forces of great power, rather than of numbers. Other considerations apart, this will be made necessary by the vulnerability of land forces to attack from the air. The only safety lies in dispersal and rapid movement. We can expect the development of many specialised vehicles, particularly tracked vehicles able to proceed across country. Tanks will increase in speed and fire power. We may expect radio-controlled tanks which will be considered "expendable." Filled with explosives they will be directed from safe positions and amount to heavy missiles travelling over the land instead of in the air. Some tanks, using special light armour, will be able to take to the air for short distances over obstacles, and small tanks able to "dig themselves in" when under attack might be designed. The increasing use of rocket-propelled missiles in the place of guns will make artillery much more mobile, for the rocket requires only a comparatively light platform for launching. Tanks with hydraulically raised guns fitted with single tracks and gyro control are another possibility.

Overshadowing everything will be developments in transport and communications. Air transport has already revolutionised land strategy and tactics but is as yet only in its early stages. The Berlin air lift has shown how lines of communication can be maintained by air. Another war might see the idea of "lines," inland fighting going by the board, with a dozen "Arnhems" on a far greater scale. Developments in radio communications will make the control of vast forces from a central headquarters more effective.

Sooner or later the jealous conception of three separate fighting forces for the land, the sea and the air will disappear. The actual distinction to-day is becoming smaller; air and sea forces transport the land forces, the armies capture or defend air or sea bases, the air forces attack the navies. Although air transport is developing rapidly, sea transport will be necessary for many years to come and its protection must increasingly be from the air. The "battleship" as we know it to-day is no doubt already obsolete except as a monitor. It can fight at a range of only about twenty miles. Warships of the future will be "floating aerodromes," capable of delivering attacks at a range of hundreds of miles. Experiments are already being carried out in propelling submarines and warships by atomic power. Success would have far-reaching effects. Hitherto they have always been dependent upon bases or a "train" for re-fuelling. With atomic power, a few pounds of "fuel" would make it possible to remain at sea for many months on end.

Between the two world wars it was thought that the submarine had begun to lose its relative power. During World War II it was used very effectively by Germany, inflicting enormous damage and making necessary the diversion of great resources. That, in the final event, it did not win a decisive victory is not likely to lead nations to underestimate its possibilities. The perfection of an underwater breathing device enabling the submarine to remain submerged, if necessary, for some months and, more important, to increase its underwater speed, has gone far to compensate for the increased vulnerability of the submarine due to radar and air attack. Indeed, the threat of the latest submarines to any power dependent upon sea transport is such that there has been a tendency to overestimate its danger. The reply to the Schnorkel breathing device will undoubtedly be found. "Homing" torpedoes following the track of reflected sound waves in the water and similar devices will make attacks on submarines, once their presence is known, very effective. The struggle between the submarine and the anti-submarine forces will continue with great ingenuity as in the last forty years, first one side and then the other seeming to have the advantage.

We must expect development of the submarine for various specialised purposes. Its great advantage is concealment and this will be very serious with the use of atomic weapons. Already tests are being carried out with troop-carrying submarines capable of transporting 250 men across the Atlantic. Submarines will be constructed capable of acting as launching platforms for missiles. They would travel, perhaps, 10,000 miles under water and then launch a rocket or bomb capable of travelling another 5,000 miles. The perfection of methods by which rockets can be launched from a submarine, even without surfacing, would mean that the submarine could acquire fire power comparable with that of a present-day warship.

The increased power of the submarine will call for entirely new defensive measures. It may be possible to make target-finding mines which would have a range of several miles. These would remain inert until "triggered" by a passing vessel, acoustically or electrically, when they would become torpedoes, "homing" on the sound or oscillation they had encountered. Such mines would make it possible to lay fields covering very much greater areas than hitherto. The breathing device which gives the submarine such great range may prove extremely vulnerable to attack with substances that, sucked in, would damage the engine or poison the atmosphere. These possibilities are mentioned merely to emphasize that no weapon is likely to be "decisive" and that there is some defence, however poor, against every attack. The importance lies in foreseeing the nature of the offensive and having a reply in readiness.

Acoustic and magnetic mines, the V1 and other so-called "secret weapons" all took heavy toll in World War II when first introduced, but in the end their effects were largely negatived. They could have been forecast long before and defences against them so planned that they would have turned out to be no surprise at all. Even the atomic bomb did not "come out of the blue." The possibility of using atomic fission "explosively" and a rough outline of the required methods was given in a magazine by an American scientific writer in 1940. As far as is known the article caused no particular interest in military circles until three years later when it was suddenly "discovered" and caused a minor panic because of the accuracy with which it anticipated events. The article was then used as a "spy trap." Military intelligence watched anyone asking for back numbers of the magazine on the rather naïve theory that they might be foreign agents.

One development in naval warfare may be the radio-controlled warship. This is not new, the old *Centurion* was radio-controlled for use as a target between the wars. But radio-control has greatly improved. At the end of World War II the U.S. had prepared a number of "robot" warships able to approach a coast unmanned and bombard specified targets. The ships transmitted back to the controlling vessels, out of range of the land, pictures of the scene in front of them. These ships were never used because the final landings planned did not have to be made, but it is certain that they have been further developed. Because the controlling devices would occupy comparatively little space and it would be unnecessary to provide quarters for the crew or provisions, it would be possible to deliver a heavy weight of fire in relation to size. Another development of "drone boats," as they are called, is the amphibian loaded with explosives and fitted with caterpillar treads so that it is capable of crawling ashore into the enemy's defences before being exploded. Drones of this type developed at the end of the war had a speed of 1 m.p.h. on water and 15 m.p.h. on land, they carried about half a ton of explosive and suggest the underwater amphibian tank as a useful alternative.

Military aircraft are developing so rapidly that it is difficult to put any limit to their speed, range, and load during the next twenty years. We must remember that the rocket-jet engine is still quite new and that it has the enormous advantage of efficiency in the stratosphere. The jet-engined plane does not, like the screw-driven plane, require air to "push against" and in the region of extremely thin air a very small amount of energy is required to give speeds of 1,000 m.p.h. or more. The immediate problems are technical, such as methods of taking planes which are efficient at 40,000 ft. up to this height without great expenditure of fuel. The way is already being shown by rocket "assisted" take-offs but these are as yet rather crude. Missiles, as distinct from planes with human crews, will become increasingly important in air attack and defence and the problem of interception when speeds rise above 700 m.p.h. has already been explained. The technique of prediction has now outstripped the speed of intercepting shells or planes, but in practice a bomber flying at 700 m.p.h. is a very difficult target for, with perfect prediction, a deviation of even half a degree by the pilot during the fifteen to twenty seconds required for the flight of the shell might imply a miss.

The interceptor and A.A. weapon of the future is likely to be a guided missile travelling at ultrasonic speeds, possibly working on a combination of the rocket and ram-jet principles. The missile would take off and reach the required height with a rocket of greater thrust than that employed in the German V2 and it would then proceed to seek out the enemy at a lower speed. Control may be by direct command from the ground, by following a radar beam between launching position and target or by "homing." A combination of two of these methods, or all three, may be required to secure the necessary accuracy.

At present the maximum height to which a rocket has ascended is 250 miles, but we must expect this distance to be rapidly increased and the problems involved in producing a man-carrying rocket will be solved in practice, as they have already been in theory. It is possible that a rocket capable of navigating in space having "escaped" from the earth will be built earlier than is generally supposed. We forget that it is not fifty years since man first flew in a heavier-than-air plane. The achievement of space flight may be of great importance to warfare, since it will make it a simple matter to attack points on the earth from a position outside the earth. It would be theoretically practicable to command the entire earth in a way not feasible from any position on the earth's surface. That this possibility is not so remote as might be thought is suggested by the announcement that the U.S. have begun serious research on a project which involves the construction of an artificial satellite some thousands of miles from the earth. This scheme was first put forward by a British engineer; there was, incidentally, a British Rocket Corps at the second siege of Boulogne.

The basis of the artificial planet idea is that if a rocket leaves the earth with the required velocity it will become a satellite, revolving round the earth like the moon. The time taken for a revolution will depend upon the "distance" from the earth, but by choosing the right distance the satellite could "keep time," as it were, always facing the same hemisphere of the world. Given four of these bodies, which would require no artificial power for their movement once they reached the chosen point, the whole earth could be covered for radio transmissions. This plan was originally put forward as a solution to the problem of long distance radio and television communication, as has been mentioned earlier in this book, but it is obvious that it also has military implications. Given radio command of the world, the ability to transmit signals to any point of it and to jam signals originating at any point, it would prove a very powerful military weapon in future warfare where radio signals of all kinds, for communications or control of missiles, will play an important or even a decisive part.

The suggestion, therefore, is that in the far future attempts may be made to set up these "platforms" and obtain control of the aether. It would be only a step further to use them as bases for launching attacks on particular parts of the world with various missiles. The data necessary for such an attack from the moon have already been prepared. No one can say whether the possibility of doing it lies ten, a hundred, or a thousand years ahead, but the conception is now taken quite seriously.

What are the advantages? At first it would appear absurd to carry missiles to a space platform or to the moon with the object of launching them at a point on the earth when they could be dispatched direct without any trouble. The advantages put forward are that it would be impossible for an enemy to know its attacker, much less to counter-attack. Missile after missile could be launched deliberately without any fear of reprisal. The moon would provide a base immune from attack. Once the necessary preparations had been made and the stores of missiles carried up, the attack could be maintained day after day. It is suggested that the psychological effect of this would be overwhelming. While there is the opportunity of reprisal or counter-measures, there is hope even in the face of the heaviest attack. But where there is no chance of being able to get at the enemy at all, surrender would seem very nearly inevitable.

The technical accuracy required for such a project is, of course, of a very high order. An error of a tenth of a mile a second in the initial velocity of the rocket might mean that the missile would land several thousand miles from the desired point on the earth. The whole work of assembling and firing the rockets would have to be done in extremely irksome conditions due to the absence of atmosphere on the moon, the very much reduced gravity and extremes of heat and cold. Against this is the fact that the propelling charge required would be small, due to the relatively low gravitational pull of the moon and the absence of air. Most of the journey to the earth would be made under the earth's attraction.

Planet attacks are no more than an interesting speculation and a common-sense view of the matter might be that if the people of the earth have not worked out some form of agreement by the time they can make a landing on the moon, they are sure to have been decimated by warfare of another nature. But, fantastic as the notion may seem, we must ask ourselves whether it is more foolish than would the launching of rockets over a course of 1,000 miles have been thought a hundred years ago. Anyone a century ago who had described a 600 m.p.h. jet bomber loaded with atomic bombs capable of completely devastating several square miles might have been regarded as a not-so-harmless lunatic. Technically, the progress that has been made does not represent anything so very different from the step from the jet bomber to a missile laden "space ship" bound for the moon.

One of the difficulties of examining the future of war is that we have recently emerged from a conflict in which so many astonishing technical advances were made. To the people who were born at a time when the aeroplane was a dream and wireless unknown, the inventions of World War II must have been almost numbing. We built artificial harbours, detected and pin-pointed aircraft hundreds of miles away, built floating aerodromes of ice, performed one technical wonder after another until nothing seemed impossible. It would be difficult to suggest any weapon of the future that would appear incredible to those who have lived through the first fifty years of the twentieth century. As far as the ordinary man to-day is concerned the danger is, perhaps, that he will believe anything to be possible in a future war rather than be thought out of date. If it were announced to-morrow that a bomb had been made with a power a million times as great as that dropped at Hiroshima, there would be few doubting voices raised. The military mind may be conservative but many of us underestimate the time required to solve technical problems and the cost in labour and materials. This means that we are very susceptible to suggestion or propaganda and we must not overlook the thought that in the "next war" much may be won by bluff.

The effect of large scale bombing was greatly over-estimated before World War II. Millions of people believed that within 24 hours of war being declared, London would be laid in ruins. They certainly did not foresee the possibility that it could be bombed night after night for months and remain habitable or even reasonably normal. It was this overestimation of the effect of an untried weapon that enabled Hitler to triumph at Munich. If he had continued to talk instead of fighting, the course of history might have been different, his "secret weapon" propaganda would have been far more effective in "peace" than in "war." Because nothing now seems impossible and because extraordinary accomplishments of science have prepared the layman to credit anything, the "next war" may see official lying reach an even higher level of accomplishment than anything we have yet encountered.

Greater size, greater speed and greater distance will be the keynotes. And to them will be added many weapons of the "new terror" type with bacteriological threats and the ever-present thought that gamma rays from atomic attack may be sterilizing our land, our cattle and ourselves. More likely in the latter case is it that attempts might be made to destroy human reproductiveness for many years beforehand until the day comes when robot-tanks begin to creep from the sea against our barrage of flaming oils and sight-destroying dust. Yet, war on our present principles of civilisation is a very natural evolutionary process and we must never be deluded by childish suggestions of ban or agreement. War is when law has failed; as well ban cancer by a law. It is so often forgotten that nearly every blessing of mankind owes its inception to warfare and that the most horrible inventions of a destructive nature can always be applied to peace, with results that benefit all civilization. There are the old but important examples of explosives for agriculture or civil engineering, radio-active isotopes for medicine and a thousand industries from face cream to engine testing, poison gas against insect pests and flame throwers for destroying weeds. Why these inventions cannot be applied to proper use in the first instance is a subject which has no place in any accurate forecast.

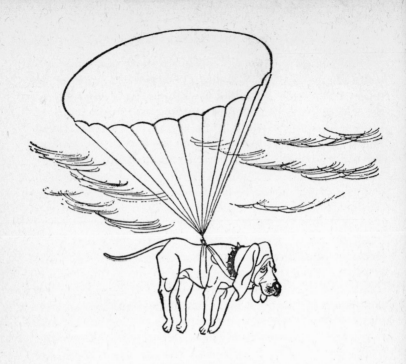

CHAPTER 9

CRIME, PUNISHMENT AND MORALS IN THE FUTURE

THE material changes already described will inevitably produce far-reaching social variations. Some qualification is necessary, for men are very conservative animals and resist change with an almost violent prejudice; even then they often propitiate the past by retaining the oldest possible terms of reference. Men resist the social, economic and legal changes which arise by scientific progress for so long that there is chaos and confusion. For reasons which no doubt were good when the law was made many centuries ago, it is still illegal to leave a parish to play games

on Sunday. Since the day when that law was made the
sedan chair has given place to the motor-car and the distance that a man can cover in an hour has changed from
the width of his own council's jurisdiction to the width of
his whole country. But the law remains; with the result
that it is completely ignored except upon the few occasions
when a common informer achieves notoriety and when
some astonished individual is reluctantly punished.

The law is, naturally, always many years behind that
elusive thing we call "public opinion," often centuries
behind discovery, and the question arises whether, in the
near future, we shall not have to consider much more
frequent alterations in our laws. In the days when the
amount of material change during a man's lifetime was
small, it did not matter very much how long a law remained on the statute books. But to-day a single invention
may completely alter circumstances in one generation and
produce a set of conditions never imagined by those who
made the rules of behaviour. Perhaps even more important, the social attitudes that really govern us far more
than the law itself have changed. Murder is no longer
common, not because of any change in the law, but because our moral values have become totally different.

Think of radio as an example of what can happen as the
result of one single invention. The law concerning slander
was formed when the worst that a man could do with the
spoken word was to shout it to a crowd of a few thousand.
To-day a man can speak to hundreds of millions and dis-
seminate his slander much further and more certainly in
a shorter time than by printing. When the laws concerning the various ways in which a man could be a traitor
were conceived the idea that he might live in the enemy's
country and daily speak to millions of his own countrymen
would have seemed fantastic, yet this was the commonest
form of treachery in the last war. The law is, of course,
extremely ingenious in its interpretation of language.

Roger Casement protested that he was being hanged for a comma. Word juggling enables the law, at least to its own satisfaction, to deal with types of offences which were unimaginable when the statutes were first laid down. But only to its own satisfaction in a measure that is neither desirable or satisfactory.

Many of the laws and rules of conduct laid down in the Old Testament, excellent in their day, have been made obsolete by scientific discovery and invention. Observance of those laws is therefore symbolical and often childish; we do not want spiritualists imprisoned under laws intended to deal with witchcraft, or recreation on Sunday governed by laws made to encourage the practise of archery several centuries ago. The comedy and chaos of the betting acts arise from the fact that laws intended to protect wealthy gamblers from card sharpers are now used to decide whether a workman may pay cash for his sixpenny bet on the Derby. The legality of operating football pools in some particular way is decided by laws conceived before pools were invented and long before anyone could imagine a newspaper being able to print four million copies.

Scientists usually disclaim any moral responsibility for their work, but it is possible that in the near future we may give advisory committees the task of examining the social or economic outlook for research so that we may be advised as to whether old laws should be amended or new laws put into effect. These committees will, we hope, not be permitted to dictate or control but rather to point out how some particular invention may lead to results which require a particular legal or moral attitude. Such an authority in the early days of motor-cars might have indicated certain very probable developments of the next fifty years and have helped us to avoid the absurdity of the Red Flag Act, the spending of millions in an attempt to make roads built for horses safe for motor-cars and of city streets so congested that motor traffic is reduced to walking pace. Scientists are by no means necessarily wise, but they are more likely to see the problems of the future than are politicians whose approach is emotional and whose view of what is likely to happen is always coloured by their personal desire.

Failure to foresee the future and to adapt ourselves physically and mentally to it has resulted in the present alarming situation where thousands of lives are lost every year and where many motorists fancy themselves in the light of persecuted martyrs. The passing of law upon law and the construction of a bewildering fantasia of signs have failed as completely to reduce the number of road accidents as has the most vigorous propaganda. But a little foresight and recognition of the motor-car as an invention bringing a profound change into our lives and habits, rather than a mere source of revenue, would have saved all this confusion. The same circumstances have arisen in the case of every major invention, even if the consequences have been less sad. Unhappily it is true that committees and other bodies of inquiry suffer so much from prejudice that their findings seldom do more than restrict progress. Medicine provides a good example, for its blessings have usually been adopted in the face of bitter opposition by useless academic dictators.

Another instance of the muddle that arises when the economic, legal and social consequences of technical progress are ignored, is to be found in our legal and penal system. This is often based upon ideas ranging over the Old Testament, Roman law and the Middle Ages. There was then no knowledge of the cause of crime, other than that it was the work of the "devil." No one really knew why crimes were committed except that they were "wicked"; the only approach made towards the investigation of crime was vaguely religious, and led to such anachronisms as the provision of chaplains to wait upon prisoners or attend them at the scaffold. During the last century an attempt was made to apply the methods of science to the mysteries of the human mind and human behaviour. Enough was learned to demonstrate that the foundations of our legal and penal system are often unsound. Yet this has had very small effect on our legal approach; we have still to maintain a vast force of police and although thousands are punished every year there are many more engaged in criminal pursuits.

The present confusion in our outlook upon capital punishment and the finding of insanity in murder cases is a good illustration. The technical attitude towards insanity has undergone a revolution in the last century, but the rules which determine "legal" insanity still cling to the days when lunatics were thrust into an open dungeon or believed to be possessed of the devil. The public to-day believes that it is inhuman and wrong to execute insane men or women. It would not be hard in the light of modern knowledge to demonstrate that any person who commits murder is insane, but our laws and our ways of thinking are nearly 300 years behind the times. We calmly ignore everything that has been learned about the mind during the present century and proceed to execute those who are "sane," that is, capable of knowing what they are doing, and therefore capable of reform. At the same time we so pamper those who are insane, that is, who suffer from disease and are virtually incurable, that a ripe old age is almost assured for anyone who is sent to Broadmoor Criminal Lunatic Asylum.

Long ago, when the question of whether a woman was enceinte was raised in the courts, a jury of matrons was impanelled to give their opinion. Although the process is still part of court procedure, we dislike getting rid of these old forms, most people would consider that a doctor qualified to make scientific tests for pregnancy would be able to give a better decision. Where the question of sanity is raised, it is still a matter for the jury, a body of worthy men no doubt, but not skilled in examination of the mind, or, for that matter, in the weighing of the highly technical evidence which is given by experts. The general principle seems to be that when a problem is difficult it is better to leave it to the decision of twelve average men than to proceed scientifically. A man who would scoff at the idea of discovering the pressure in his car tyre by any means but a gauge will confidently give his opinion on the sanity or insanity of a man after listening to the arguments of lawyers; as if words could either establish or change facts.

The study of the mind is still in its infancy, but during the last thirty years some progress has been achieved. What often before seemed unreasoning is now beginning to appear orderly and as capable of interpretation in terms of cause and effect as are other phenomena. In the future this will have a profound effect, both on our laws and in our dealings with those who break convention. Modern punishments will seem as stupid and barbarous as cutting off hands or torturing and breaking on the wheel. It is only by substituting the scientific for the emotional approach to crime and punishment that we shall gain lasting results. After centuries of punishments, which have merely varied in severity, we still have a huge prison population and few would dispute that the general standard of morality as measured by the observance of the laws is as low as it has ever been before. An emotional approach to a social problem, such as crime, can no more solve it than would a decision that nine is the square of sixty-seven because it is a "lucky" number. The alchemists of the Middle Ages sought results by methods which seem laughable to a modern schoolboy because they were more concerned with emotion than science and fact. Our way of dealing with criminals is not a fine example of progress in any direction.

In the future, we shall be far less ready to contemplate

our over-full prisons with all the waste that is implied, or to think so complacently of a large police force and a vast amount of undetected crime. People will decide to face the facts instead of giving vent to the feelings inherited from tribal days. The change is not likely to be dramatic, for although we may accept the fact of material discovery readily enough we find it difficult to adapt our mental attitude without long delay. The public, it seems, will not demand the abolition of capital punishment, but they might tacitly agree to the reprieve of every murderer. In some countries, although capital punishment is the law, there has been no execution for fifty years. This is an example likely to be imitated before long; only a few years ago hanging for theft was considered to be very proper.

Before long other means will be sought for "curing" criminals than by imprisoning them with their fellows, putting them on a low diet and providing harsh discipline or meaningless work. Looking back we may consider it fantastic that our parents persisted in such treatment in spite of its continued failure to bring results through so many centuries. Our belief that criminals might be changed by the sapping of their mental and physical health might be explained in the supposition that we were sub-consciously satisfying a primitive instinct for revenge rather than attacking the problem of crime. As for the "deterrent" element in punishment our children will laugh at the idea that only the periodical execution of murderers and the imprisonment of embezzlers or biga-mists prevented every man from killing his neighbour, stealing his employer's money and marrying three wives at a time.

A society, tired of being troubled by persistent offenders, will decide to examine the problem scientifically. They will decide that the remedy for stupidity, and although we call them "clever" only the stupid law-breakers are caught, is not to shut them up with other peculiar specimens, under-feeding them and giving work that provides neither interest nor reward, but to seek the cause of this stupidity. Perhaps it will be decided that all criminals must be abnormal, otherwise the majority of people would indulge in crime. It may be found that in many cases the cause of the failing intelligence is organic and can be corrected. A defective diet may be responsible, or various over-active or insufficiently active glands may be blamed. Unbalance of the endocrine system produces strange results. Even the idea of blaming a virus for criminal impulses would sound no more absurd to-day than it would have appeared ridiculous to credit scurvy to the lack of a minute substance in the diet of a century ago.

In many cases, no doubt, it will be found possible to correct abnormality. The E.E.G., the "brain wave" recording device, can already observe an abnormality in children which is often easy to correct but which if left untreated might well result in the child growing up as an habitual criminal. Systematic research may reveal that there are surprisingly few cases of crime that cannot be attributed to physical or mental abnormalities capable of surgical or medical treatment. Those in whom no apparent cause can be found will be regarded as of exceptional interest, and observation will probably pave the way to further discoveries. It is an appalling reflection that with some 20,000 men and women permanently in our prisons, and with every opportunity for research under controlled conditions, the main interest of medicine seems that of finding who is fit to undergo corporal punishment and who to live on bread and water. There are no chairs or schools of scientific penology and the criterion by which a prison official is judged is not how many criminals he corrects but how many he prevents from obeying their natural impulse to escape.

Changes will obviously embrace the courts as well as prisons. It will be considered fantastic for judges to order punishments of which they have no real knowledge, only a very few of our magistrates and judges have ever regularly visited prisons or witnessed flogging or hanging. This will be considered as unscientific as a doctor ordering a medicine of which he has no knowledge at all but which he has heard to be the "right thing." Courts will be concerned not only in ordering punishments but in considering treatment. They may advise so many months of sedatives, as modern courts order so many months' imprisonment. They will certainly attempt to make the treatment fit the cause of the crime and not the crime itself; they will not delude themselves that the man who has committed bigamy, the man who has killed another as the result of carelessness and the man who has burgled a bank will all benefit by the same retribution. Work will be allotted as carefully as a doctor prescribes for a patient recovering from a severe illness. In many cases, no doubt, it will be found that the opportunity to make amends will be part of the cure. To-day we talk of a thief "paying his debt to society," but never let him pay his debt to the wronged. The bigamist may swindle two women and we make it worse by depriving him of the opportunity to support either of the sufferers.

A court will not always require men to wear fancy dress or false hair to give them importance. Counsel will not try only to prove that a man is guilty or innocent but will attempt to discover whether or not he requires treatment. Examination will be as unemotional as that of a surgeon who examines a patient suspected of some operable abnormality, and the relationship of judge and prisoner will eventually become more that of doctor and patient. The positions of judges to-day will be considered as absurd as that of a doctor who, knowing nothing but the name of a coughing patient, forthwith orders a severe thoracic operation. To discover the truth by employing advocates to pit their wits against each other will seem as ludicrous a century hence as the "science" of the Middle Ages, based upon prejudice and superstition, appears to us to-day.

Such a change of attitude suggests the possibility that judges may one day be willing to discuss abnormal tendencies with criminals prior to the commission of crime. Perhaps there will be clinics where those who have broken the law, or feel the impulse to do so, can secure expert advice. If it is found necessary for them to become "inpatients," little more will be thought of it than as an entry to a nursing home. Fanciful perhaps, but no greater advance in comparison than are our methods to-day from the time of trial by ordeal. Failure to make changes in our outlook upon crime will mean the growth of a permanent criminal class, parasitic on society and demanding the expenditure of vast sums in the interests of self-protection.

A discovery that may have far-reaching effects, possibly harmful unless it is well considered, is the modern technique of artificial insemination. That this subject should have been discussed by the House of Lords is in itself a sign of progress; fifty years ago the topic would have been thrown out as unfit for public discussion and a law would have been passed forbidding everything to do with so startling an innovation, an "innovation" which, by the way, was known in Ancient Greece. It is mainly the principle of concealment which resulted in venereal disease becoming so great a menace long after the discovery of scientific means for a majority cure. Even to-day, when much more certain and simple methods of prevention and cure exist for this scourge, fear of outspoken comment has so hindered science that thousands die unnecessarily and still more are incapacitated at an early age.

The insemination debate in the House of Lords brought no conclusion although a simple recognition that new discoveries must profoundly affect our lives, in the ethical as well as the material sense, was in itself noteworthy. The traditional method of all legislative bodies has been to

ignore new and awkward facts until these have made themselves so painfully felt that hasty and often ill-devised
corrective measures must be taken. Too little and too
late. In justice it should be added that our legislators
have been truly representative; the public regards facts
which shatter deep-seated notions as "unpleasant" and
prefers to shut its eyes rather than to learn. New generations will be better educated, better taught to observe or
think and more willing to be concerned with modern truth
than with inaccurate history.

As an example of the harmful results that come from
ignoring the truth let us take one "fact" that has been
obvious for many years, but which is still almost disre-
garded in our ethics and law. Intelligent men and women
can to-day decide whether they will or will not have children. Thousands of couples marry without the slightest
intention of having children and children are no longer
inevitably, or even usually, the result of extra-marital
association. But our ethical and legal systems continue as
if the modern man and woman had as little choice in the
matter of children as had their great-grandparents. The
man who "has his quiver full" is still considered as deserv-
ing of congratulations, even of public charity, although
all the children may be mentally deficient and although
it is well known that he is not "blessed" but stupid, lazy
or improvident.

The barbaric stigma of illegitimacy, rising divorce figures, a birthrate with no relation to economics, increasing
mental deficiency and decreasing average intelligence;
these and other problems will never be truly faced, much
less solved, until new facts are openly recognised. Instead,
there will be legal tinkering, the introduction of easier and
easier divorce, or abolition of the legal, but not social,
handicaps of illegitimacy.

Unless we readjust our application of temporary facts,
civilised nations may soon be faced with difficulties that are

only just becoming apparent but which will be almost impossible to correct without war when firmly established. The elimination of defective stocks, effected in a wild state by natural selection, is largely negatived by medicine and "social services." The result is that what the geneticist calls "deleterious mutations" survive and will increasingly continue to do so. If this process is unchecked, to use the words of Huxley, "Humanity will gradually destroy itself from within, will decay in its very core and essence." It is better to recognise evolution than to pretend that inefficiency can be changed by the aid of social heredity alone.

The obvious remedy is to observe the truth and to reverse the financial, economic and social handicaps imposed by legislators who mainly consult their own prejudices. If there is any real link between success and a chosen rate of low fertility it should be studied dispassionately rather than by those who are swayed by emotion or by the sentimental demand that the "unfortunate" shall inherit, not the kingdom of heaven, but the earth. There are already signs in civilised countries of a slow fall in the average level of intelligence. This is very difficult to assess and although the methods involved are somewhat empirical there are strong indications that the reduction in reproduction rates is selective and that those of low intelligence are likely to have the most numerous families. When the large family is partly supported by the small, this tendency is increased and if we continue to ignore the well-established science of genetics in this fashion our experience of animals under comparable circumstances will prove in vain.

There is yet another problem that the future must face. Some progress has been made in sex determination. Before very long it may occasionally be possible for parents to choose for themselves whether they will have a boy or a girl. The natural processes by which the ratio between male and female population is maintained could then, to some extent, be in the hands of men to control. Will future generations face this challenge and decide how it should affect their laws and social behaviour, or will they bury their heads and declare that it is "unnatural" until the time comes when chaos threatens? It might be too late to achieve what seems immediately desirable by selective taxation, the offer of bribes or even the state ordering of sex. We have only to consider that, at present, when parents can choose the sex of their adopted children the demand is ten times as great for girls as boys, to see the grave economic implications that will arise if sex selection becomes generally practicable.

Future generations will have to think of the profound ethical and political results that may follow the establishment of new physiological practices. The probabilities for the near future include the determination of sex, the bearing of children by women by an unknown father, and the grafting of living tissue from one person to another, to an extent which now seems miraculous. The average man has hardly given a thought to the troubles that arise from artificial insemination. It will be possible for a single man to be the father of many thousands of children by different women. Indeed, while the present attitude continues, that there is something rather disgraceful about A.I.D., the probability is that one man will be used as the donor in a large number of cases because of the difficulty of finding volunteers. From this will flow various consequences, such as the artificial perpetration of certain unwanted stocks or the chance of unintentional in-breeding. Our legislators are so busy discussing whether a man may marry his divorced wife's sister that they do not worry to make sure that he cannot marry his own daughter produced by A.I.D.

The amazing possibilities of grafting have already been explained but think, once again, of the legal repercussions. Modern surgeons are developing great skill and they are assisted by a mass of new mechanical, chemical or electrical devices. Nerves have been transplanted into a limb to replace one severed or damaged beyond repair; in Russia where this method was adopted during the war, nerves were taken from people killed in accidents after attempts to use animal "tissue" had failed. To the scientist there may seem nothing wrong, but it is not hard to imagine the protests or even lynchings that might occur if this plan was introduced in a country where the lifeless body is considered so sacred that more money may be spent on its disposal than upon the same body when alive. It may be found in the future that the thousands who die prematurely every year in accidents are not wholly wasted, that they could give health and perhaps new hope of life to thousands of others by means of a graft.

Our immediate reaction might be to ask for such operations to be made illegal and we should have a situation resembling that which occurred when anatomists first needed bodies for dissection. "Body snatchers" ran a flourishing market because legal transactions were impossible. In the near future some regulation of what may be permitted in surgical grafting will be required. The time has come when such simple operations as the provision of a new cornea, a "gland sector" or an ear are common. But surgery is a comparatively new art and with the discoveries of science, sensational advances happen almost daily. Should we be able to purchase spare parts for our bodies? Would not an advertisement offering £1,000 bring offers of limbs and other useful features which may soon be well within our power to transplant?

Much the same situation exists to-day in the instance of "illegal" operations. The law cannot prevent such operations from being performed, it only succeeds in driving them underground. The result of the law has not been to save lives but to take them, for the operations are often carried out unskilfully by ignorant people. Instead of having the high-minded results expected by those who framed the law, the consequences are sordidness, pain, death and a rich living for the unscrupulous.

The law is hopelessly out of date in its findings upon legitimacy, artificial or otherwise, for this seems to vary from country to country; a child may be legitimate in America and not in England. These are not matters to be settled by ex-communications and debate but by fact. Supposing a man, desiring no heir, is made to produce a child after his death by relatives who own the body. The example is worthy of repetition. Should we wait for an appeal to the Lords or receive instructions as to what is best done from an obscure chapter from the Old Testament?

To ignore facts is not a remedy. Inventions cannot be legislated out of existence and it is only by full presentation of the facts to the public that a proper solution of the problems caused by progress can be decided. Future men and women will not be hynotised by words and slogans as are we to-day. To condemn these new practices as against nature is to take refuge in an outmoded phrase. It is the word-magic of the tribal medicine man dressed in twentieth-century clothing. An aluminium leg is "unnatural"; so is an operation for appendicitis or the use of disinfectants. It is history that anaesthetics were condemned as irreligious, and although this is not a common view to-day many mothers-to-be suffer from the old prejudice. The generations to come will soon regard physiological processes as an extension of the control over environment which has helped man to retain his position as the most successful of all animals. Materially and legally, control of our species may be regarded as a very natural development of the process of selection for which the "artificiality" of Rhesus tests before marriage are a useful form of insurance.

CHAPTER 10

WHERE DO WE GO FROM HERE?

THE very definite outlook already described suggests that we may look for considerable material advance, no greater, however, than that which we have experienced during the last fifty years. These things are bound to happen, as will be agreed, apart from details, by the majority of thinking people. The prospect can be a world from which much pain and hard labour have been abolished, a world with an abundance of food, shelter and the means of enjoying life. Yet there are many who show little interest, for, and this may apply less strongly to youth, the prevailing mood of millions to-day is one of insecurity.

It is a paradox of the mid-twentieth century that never before have so many people enjoyed so many possessions and never before has there been so much talk of undesirable change. We have the means for transporting goods and people from country to country on an unprecedented scale and with uncanny ease; at the same time it has never been so difficult for actual goods and people to move. Restrictions on travel are far greater in practice than in the Middle Ages when men could travel only on foot or horseback. Never before has there been the same prospect of material progress and prosperity and never before have so many people feared the future. We have medical knowledge and services vastly superior to those of a hundred years ago, yet hospitals and doctors' surgeries are filled to overflowing with the sick. All the signs are that the man of the near future could enjoy a standard of life that in many respects was available only to the wealthiest prince a century ago, but the prevailing spirit is not one of welcoming a "brave new world" but of utter pessimism.

This is a passing phase. There have been greater and more rapid changes in the fifty years of this century than in any century that has passed since the Renaissance. The "industrial revolution," with the far-reaching changes it brought, was comparatively slow. It was spread, not over a lifetime, but over several generations. Each person in his life had to carry out only so much adjustment in his manners, ideas and outlook. Even so these alterations were in many respects painful and now, with far greater speed in the world's thought, it is impossible for many people to keep pace. We cannot take it for granted that older people are more conservative and less able to alter their habits than the young, but it is broadly true that they hold the greater proportion of control where power and influence are concerned. A new generation is growing up that will assume as normal many of the things to which we have had to adapt ourselves in the course of a decade. A motor-car seemed hopelessly intricate to the old coachman who found himself out of employment, and already a car is less complicated than a horse to the average man. There are still millions who cannot regard a wireless set as anything but a mysterious box of tricks, but there are more millions growing up who see no greater difficulty in following a radio circuit than in obeying the traffic directions on an arterial road.

All these are reasons for the idea, subconsciously held by many, that "life is becoming too complicated." Man is finding it very much easier to adapt his environment than to adapt himself. The example of road casualties has been quoted. It takes some years for laboratory discoveries to percolate into general acceptance by the "man-in-the-street." As another instance, it is long since the time when science established that a number of diseases were transmitted by organisms passed from person to person. But we still do not act as if this were an indisputable fact. It is a serious offence to hit a harmless stranger over the head with your walking stick, but it is considered no more than bad manners to sneeze or cough in his face and to spit in the street is not even thought to be a breach of manners in many circles. Possibly a century after Pasteur's discoveries it will no longer be important to put up notices "Penalty for spitting 50 shillings" for the same reason as it is now unnecessary to display notices "Do not commit murder; penalty—death."

One notable cause of modern discontent is the complete failure of the so-called "social sciences" to keep abreast of "material" discovery. Economics, psychology and politics are, in fact, not yet sciences at all; they bear the same relation to normal science as does alchemy to atomic physics, witchcraft to modern medicine or astrology to astronomy. They are such a strange mixture of fact, hypothesis and emotion that it is hardly surprising to find that while we know how to produce vast quantities of food, we have no idea how to arrange for its distribution and that although we have less reason than ever to covet a neighbour's land we are constantly on the verge of war. These "political" matters are not sciences at all in the sense of chemistry or physics. They are not even applied sciences such as engineering. If we used the technique of the politician and psychologist in building bridges it would be a matter of good fortune and not certainty if they bore the loads for which they were designed.

A very necessary development of the future, if we are to benefit from progress and not to collapse under its consequences, must be a far better investigation of the causes of individual and group behaviour. We have only the haziest notions of the motive power of human thought and action; we suffer from the same handicaps as a man with an engine who does not know what fuel it requires. The foundation of original research on these lines will be all the more difficult because we have already built up so many tremendous social structures; the world is full of economists who know all the answers and who enjoy a jargon rivalling that of the medieval soothsayer. The complication of politics has baffled us until we imagine the only way to decide any point is to allow everyone, good, bad and indifferent, to give his opinion; on the theory no doubt, that the majority cannot then complain or that they have been given "the government they deserved." Imagine a chemist, unable to decide what he should add to what to synthetize some desired chemical, calling all his friends, none of whom had ever studied chemistry, and asking them to vote on the subject. Half the countries in the world base their science of government on this thrilling plan.

If a physicist propounds a "law," we may be reasonably certain that wherever and however it is applied, the result will be as indicated by that law. A single exception invalidates the rule and the whole test depends upon the principle of continued application. But economics depends upon all kinds of assumptions and alleged laws which, as soon as they are stripped of their absolutes and applied to men and women, pounds of flour or coins of the realm, fail to operate. The amount of "fact" upon which every economist will agree is trifling. For the rest, they belong to "schools" and their dogmatism savours of religion rather than science. This indeed, may be no fault, the trouble arises when the belief is treated as truth and the public calls down fire from heaven instead of striking a match.

Psychology, in danger of becoming an almost useless series of unsupported speculations clothed as unintelligibly as possible, is achieving some sanity by experiment, almost the only foundation of science. If it can show us the way in which men can adapt themselves to environment, it will be of the greatest value. Far-reaching changes have to be made in the relationship of men and women with each other and with their families who, whether at work or play, are living under conditions which bear no relation to past experience. Consider again an instance where applied psychology could be of immediate and practical service, that is, in the study of accidents in the home, for few accidents are really accidental. What is it that makes people susceptible to chance injury? How can they be warned or cured? This is an opportunity for research which should be taken up with the resolve that no jargon, no dialectical skill and no fascinating hypothesis be allowed to distract attention from fact.

It is worth recalling the story of Charles II's question to the Royal Society in the formation of which he played so important a part. According to the tale, he set the learned members a question: "Why was it that a new laid egg floated, but a boiled egg sank?" The society went into conference. For days they debated the question, anxious to please their patron, until at last they had to reply that they could not find a true reason. Charles II's reply was concise, "It does not." One simple experiment would have solved the problem and no doubt the lesson was learned. In matters dealing with the behaviour of men there are still millions who seek truth by debate and who have not grasped that no technical knowledge has ever been gained other than by observation. Every possibility may be argued, but nothing is of use until tested by observation. The social and economic muddle in which we find the world and which has caused so much pessimism as to the future, suggests that our approach to difficulty has been completely unscientific. Prejudices and preconceived beliefs still count with many, far more than the finding of truth by experiment.

In Russia, the belief that words are realities is leading to a quaint situation where the "truth" of a discovery is to be tested, not by observation, but by whether or not it can be associated with certain pre-conceived axioms. If it does not fit, then it is not "true," even if it happens. No new discovery must "contradict" what is stated by authority, and if it chances to do so, then it has not been discovered or, as lawyers would say, if it has, it is false. One is reminded of Galileo's recantation and his supposed whisper "Nevertheless it moves." In the end these absurdities are bound to be found out to the ultimate undoing of those who cling to prejudice. It is easy, for example, to imprison or execute every person who believes that sexual heredity is more important than environment. But this does not alter facts and the relative positions of breeding and circumstances are exactly the same as before. It is because we cannot alter facts, but only discover them, that complete freedom to experiment, to publish and to debate are so important. It is ability to survive that will settle the fate of economics, politics and sociology.

There is one other important cause for lack of faith in

the future: lack of purpose. Faith in the dogmatic religions has waned and millions, if not the majority, are no longer prepared to accept theological explanations of the purpose of living. Science may have helped to destroy faith; this was inevitable as soon as scientific method was applied. But science offered no new creed which could be accepted at face value. Humanitarianism is more subtle than dogma and thus it was that political and economic religions began to take precedence. Debates were no longer concerned with man being born in sin, but as to whether men were born equal. People are persuaded that all they need to be "saved" is a belief in a particular political system; millions adopt these easy faiths and for a time are completely satisfied.

Unfortunately the new priesthoods promise the "kingdom of heaven," not hereafter but now, and their disciples are liable to disillusionment. No one has ever been able to decide if any human being has arrived in a theoretical paradise as a result of obeying the laws of a sect. But it is simple to test whether someone is happier in following a known series of material laws, and there is no doubt that if human beings were able to act with a scientific sense of honour they would find no difficulty in seeing their own purpose in life. Very few to-day are satisfied to rely upon faith alone. They feel that the power of thought is there to be used and that if we have no wings we have brains to devise aircraft. It is by the same token we cannot trust any religion which is incompatible with our sense of observation.

It may be many years, but the time will come when we will be unwilling to regulate our lives in detail upon a book which was written many years after the events it presumes to reveal in days when no permanent record was possible. Men will demand, but never receive, an explanation of the grossly contradictory statements which human beings attribute to the Almighty in order to serve their own ends. They will look with suspicion upon any common belief which is based upon pagan sacrifice and it will not take them long to find that the simple truths of nearly all religions are greater than the human interpretation in the "closed shop" of those who profess intimacy with the wishes of an all powerful, but occasionally helpless, Creator.

It is by observation and experience that we see kindness, gentleness and humility to be the "true" virtues in the sense that their exercise never fails to bring the desired results. Mankind has often repudiated dogmatic religious authority as a reason for humanitarian conduct but has not troubled to pursue this matter further and, in general, has merely substituted new superstitions for old. We venerate the majority and believe in the pathetic statement that twenty million people cannot be wrong. Five-year plans are greeted as divine revelations and every politician can find listeners when he cries, "Follow me and be saved." It is almost universally believed that we have only to find the right "system" for every problem to be solved.

What will become more widely understood in the future is that material prosperity is in itself quite purposeless. A family that is moved from a slum to a modern flat, complete with every device that science can produce, is not thereby made better, but is simply given the opportunity to become better. It is of no importance to "save time" unless we know what to do with the time saved. We are like misers, or greedy children, grasping everything we can reach, sometimes feeling satiated, but never satisfied. That is the greatest lesson, apart from our own ignorance, that is appreciated by the majority of scientists. Science is not in itself an end, it is only the means to an end.

The ideal of "every family with its car and every pot with its chicken" may be excellent, if it is grasped that this somewhat gross definition is no more than a minor part of true civilisation. Forty years ago it was fashionable to say that we were in danger of being enslaved by the machines we created and pictures were conjured up of "robots" taking charge of the world. There is not the slightest chance of this happening in the literal sense, but there is a danger that we may fail to see the object for which we labour so hard. Applied science has always been considered "progress" and in the past the benefits it has brought have sometimes in themselves justified the claim. But with the vast possibilities of technical advancement to-day, we should consider that progress implies a going forward to something which may be good or bad according to its ultimate goal. At the moment, most of us have given the destination no thought at all. It is sufficient that we are "progressing."

It is not true or sensible that a halt should be called to science. Such an argument is based on the assumption that discovery has made us no happier and that the dangers implied by invention are greater than the benefits likely to be derived. This is in itself a childish idea for, if a reference to warfare is intended, it has long been clear that peace is equally involved. Happiness cannot be measured, but science has certainly made people healthier and wealthier in thought and these are good things on which to build. As for danger, every invention since the beginning of time has brought with it new alarms. The first weapons made it easier for men, not only to protect themselves from wild beasts, but also to kill each other more quickly. The discovery of anaesthetics made possible painless surgery, also the use of chloroform by criminals. Scientists, perhaps, are to blame for not having insisted before upon the matter of responsibility. They claimed neutrality and explained that discovery would end if law attempted to define the field in which research was permitted. It is the lack of true scientific training which renders us unable to foresee the result of any action and it is the half-training by rule or examination which brings us to neglect the consequences of our thought.

Much of our present chaos has arisen through failure to foresee the future. In the past those who have attempted to forecast the future on scientific principles and to warn that certain discoveries made certain events inevitable, have been ignored or heard with a sceptical smile. The study of the future now becomes of vital importance and an amusing example has been given as the result of our attempts to harness tidal power. If this could be accomplished without consideration of the amount of power taken, it might result, after thousands of years, in the earth being destroyed by collision with the moon. The moral is that although consequences may be far ahead, once the decision is taken they are almost inevitable. In the future we must learn a far greater sense of responsibility and "we," as the advertisements say, means "you."

That the course of science can somehow be reversed, that a holiday from invention and discovery would benefit us, does not bear examination. It has been possible to discourage the scientific spirit by persecution and by maintaining ignorance and superstition which are the only alternatives to science. But these cannot last and that is why untrammelled research is inevitable; only our reaction to its result is beyond the vision of any human being. The wish to take some personal part in guiding the world is growing every day. Thought is even more important than action and it is safe to trust that out of our gropings will come a sense of direction which will not only bring us advantages in a lifetime but help us peaceably to enjoy them every one.

CONCLUSION

THERE is no true conclusion to anything. Certainly not to a world which will soon be changed out of all recognition. It is for this very reason that we should accustom our minds to think entirely in terms of change, for if we could grow tortoise eyes in place of our present butterfly vision we should be able to watch all our surroundings as they crumbled to dust like a felled chimney in a newsreel.

We could watch a forest fade as creeping weeds killed its strength, or see ourselves change in methods of thought, in clothing, colour, and even in shape. Nothing is ever without change for the minutest fraction of time. To study change is to project time. We can move forwards or backwards along this curve as if we alternately read paragraphs from the family album and an American pocket digest. Even our own lives provide us with contrast enough to decide our position on this vast calendar; backed by a few events from history, geographical record and obvious evolution. It is then a simple matter to see change and, if we can neglect prejudice, to follow a trend where prejudice is the only barrier.

But we are still very ignorant and difficult to move. There appeared not long ago an account of police-court proceedings in which the chairman of a bench, hearing a boy confuse his words when taking the oath, remarked "Do you not know who Almighty God is?" "No, sir," said the boy. The magistrate turned to his colleagues and remarked, "Here we are spending tens of thousands of pounds every year on educating these people and this boy does not even know who God is." If only the poor child had been a little less nervous it would have been delightful to hear him reply, "No, sir, please who is He?"

Prejudice is a very evil thing. But unless the outlook of mankind has totally altered within the last hundred years our children will still laugh at us with the air of pity which we reserve for Man Friday, for those of whom we read in drawer-lining newspapers or on the leaves from journals used to prevent the ingress of dirt to the backs of old pictures. Indeed, it is a useful and humiliating experience to read such things.

Those who say that "science has gone too far" or that "machinery has reared its ugly head" are merely platitudinous bores. For we are still savage. Our throats are fishlike, our thoughts depend upon a full stomach, our teeth and claws are evident every time we see ourselves in a bath. Poor animals that waste ninety-five per cent of electricity to make light, seventy-five per cent of fuel to produce power and whose near forbears burned witches at the stake. Monkeys are just behind on the next train.

Remember a few examples of our sloth. How near we were to possessing a record of the Sermon on the Mount; or how easy for crystal sets to have been made in the time of Henry VIII, when far better workmanship was available than is much we use to-day. Remember that doctors were not allowed to bring children into the world and that a physician who attended one of these distressing events disguised as a female nurse was afterwards burned for his trouble.

Only a century ago medical authorities stated, agreement being reached for once, that travelling at sixty m.p.h. would be fatal to human beings, and it is now only fatal to those who do not do so. Closer home was our Admiralty with its decision that steam would ruin the Navy. Do we seriously imagine that with all the modern tools of science we have reached finality or that progress has ceased? Can we not see that even so simple a thing as clothing, used for defence and for decoration, is now more "utility"? Can we not grasp that time is short and that we must be prepared for easily observed change?

Comparisons are necessary to make this clear because we are all so extraordinarily conservative and inclined to hope that nothing can alter, other than by our own permission. So think back a little. Do you now admire food gluttons and polite belchings as much as when food was all in all, or are we now a little disgusted by the enthusiast? That is a point on our time curve, for it can be produced forward to the day when foods are designed and restricted in accordance with the work they eventually produce. We all know not to expect tabloid feeding, or electrical energy put into us while we sleep, for countless centuries, because the machinery of the body has to be worked in order that it can absorb a fraction of the nourishment we take; but we no longer admire bodies and powerful frames alone.

Think of anaesthetics, bitterly opposed not long ago, and see that pain is gradually being taken from our lives. Consider religion and realise that we are no longer content with forms and symbols in our churches. Notice that even sport is changing at the same headlong speed. The day will come when mechanical games interest better people than loafers wasting thought upon the stupidest of large domestic animals. Do we really believe that men will always be content to shout encouragement to dogs as they run after an electrically driven dummy? These are only a few little items in the history of the future which it is worth-while to recapitulate.

There are so many things which could have been foreseen and it is almost as easy to look forward to-day as from the time when magic lanterns and silent pictures were popular. Anyone could see, never mind how for the moment, that talking films were certain, just as to-day it is clear that television will obviate the need for us to drag our bodies about the world. In the far future we shall lose the desire to walk, we shall have teeth extracted at birth and have very little hair. We shall have flying cars and, above all, our speed of thought and communication will have increased, for that is the main difference between ourselves and old time savages. We make appointments now and say, "I can give you a few minutes." "At the full of the moon" used to be sufficiently accurate.

If we were looking very far ahead it would be so easy to plot out many sensational developments that are very sure to come: streets with covered ways; travelling pavements; roofs for aero landings; warmed streets and roads, some are already in use, to avoid dislocation of traffic by frost. Radar for railways is overdue; for a country to be blotted out by fog is pitiful even in our time.

Comfort is also a very vital factor—comfort and speed. We shall lose much of the desire for physical effort. Electrically warmed clothing, protection for the skull, more aids to sight and vision and all clothing more related to sense. It cannot be long before we are able to wear garments which are not ruined by water and which can be freed from bacteria every day. This tendency is here already and most of us would like to wear simple clothes if only our friends would not think that we suffered from exhibitionism and that by no other means could we draw attention to our importance.

It is ludicrous that we should case our bodies in a collection of expensive bits or wear soft black and hard white because we wish to enjoy a meal in company with our friends; and a microscopic examination of our best trousers would soon prove that they should never be worn without cleaning for more than a day. Not that our germ and animal soiled streets would be permitted in a future where air will be recognised as something not to be dirtied without reason. Personal freedom will have to be restricted in many ways, and we shall not always be allowed to make noises in other people's ears any more than we can now spit through a neighbour's open window.

It would be easy to continue almost indefinitely with descriptions of change and fashion, love, travel, electrical apparatus, electronic aircraft lifting and even those geographical effects which we call morals. But let us rest content with a few more general examples and begin with the case of building. We still erect many of our houses almost in the fashion of mud huts, lump by lump; whereas they could be poured almost wall by wall. It is true that there are circumstances where this form of expenditure has been made worthless by control so that there is not likely to be very rapid architectural progress in the immediate future.

In a small country where space is so important we shall soon begin to build in our parks with the advantage that there will be less beauty for people to destroy. Vast congregations of flats will certainly spring up. They will be fitted with television, hot water, pneumatic post tubes and perhaps even milk laid on from a central depot; everything will be done to prevent the need for visiting one's neighbours in person. The inhabitants will be provided with automatic clocks and possibly watches controlled from a broadcasting station to demonstrate the value of time. The change in accuracy which has already taken place in this respect is worth mentioning, for it is only a few hundred years since Columbus used to spit over the side of his ship and time with his pulse how long it took to float by. We are much more careful now.

Before long the world will care very much less for display and a number of modern professions will be entirely vulgarised. Air pilots, to quote an instance, will be reduced, or is it promoted, to the status of engine drivers because there will be very little for them to do in the automatic aircraft of the future. As for archaic ceremony or play, nearly all our love for the past will disappear and this, in some ways, may be good. Better to see an annual celebration of the date when penicillin was discovered to save lives than to honour the battle of Waterloo and D-day of which the main purpose was precisely the opposite.

We shall all of us become very lazy, physically and such pastimes as dancing, which seems to have originated for religious or sexual purposes, will be looked upon with surprise. True, dancing may be silent with an artistic rhythm, instilled into the performers by means of headphones or even direct to the brain, in a fashion as incomprehensible as Picasso to a less modern. It is even possible that our oscillating floor may arrive sooner than expected for we are willing to do anything to save trouble and the effect of relative motion would call for less effort. The human body is very susceptible to mechanical movement and when mechanised by electrically driven hearts and lungs with a development of the modern experimental machine which can maintain the functions of a patient's kidneys long enough for his own fittings to be corrected, much time will be saved. Livers and kidneys cannot yet be grafted but this may be a trifling detail to the surgeon of the future.

Perhaps it would be happier if a few pleasures of the coming years were summarised. Here they are: trips for the week-end to Africa; New York in two hours; a Channel tunnel; an automatic voting system with electronic calculators so that a government can go to the country on any minor question in the space of one day; telephones, but no tickets, on trains; totally different systems of coal mining; abolition of capital punishment; radio gramophones operated on the micro-photographic principle so that an opera can be contained in a pillbox; pocket radio; growth control; artificial gems; tidal power; men and women less easily distinguishable and with far greater freedom in their relation to the problem of marriage or morals.

It will be a world of relative silence where we shall spend many hours seeking to find out how life may be prolonged. Our attitude towards cells which cease to co-operate and snatch some of us away in the midst of things that matter will no longer be treated as a religious problem but as something which is worth a fight. We shall not continue to live lives of physical self-satisfaction or use drugs to excite sensations which should long have been forgotten.

If evolution has its way, and politics cannot stop it, we shall seek new forms of competition in the hope of replacing the ant-like existence which so many now enjoy. We shall be interested in such things as further sub-divisions of atomic structures, not for war and power, but for their direct bearing upon the secrets of life, with which the movements of electrons will soon be identified. Everything in this world is living. It is only the rate of life which varies and it is the speed at which thought brings us into the world of physical disabilities which decides all personality. We are so undeveloped that we regard drought, famine or flood as an act of God, when we really mean that our brains do not act quickly enough to vis-ualise a remedy.

We shall waste far less time when thought, or even matter, is transferable and when we are so highly trained that the minds of others are able to affect us. Perhaps we shall not always have to waggle our lips and blow air through them to communicate with our fellow creatures in a chain of life where only a few landmarks can be seen. To a student of evolution the world of vegetation was bound to lead to some rapidly living creatures like our-selves. But the process takes time and if we are glad that we were not born when trees, worms, fish, flowers and monkeys were our shape, we must not forget that our "final" form is just as far away, for the earth's pudding is still warm in the middle. It was said, not long ago, that technicians had found that the stars do not always keep to their courses. What incomparable vanity to think that we know what these courses should be.

Thoughts, in spite of recent claims, cannot yet be controlled by the aether, although it can be established that some effect can be observed outside the confines of physical bodies. Perhaps thought is permanent; perhaps thought can create; perhaps the time will come when wrong thinking is punishable. It might even be that, when the radiophone rings in the far future, a voice will answer for us without excuses and say quietly, "He cannot be disturbed, he is thinking." Which is quite a sensible ending for any book. Better, at least than trying to define all that we do not know or all we cannot dream, such as the spherical problems of the world, infinity, space or its purpose and whether or no the atom is itself an inhabited universe. The greatest lesson of the past century has not yet been learned by every scientist. It is that the sum of our present knowledge is virtually nothing at all.